How to Do Your Own
Home Insulating

by L. Donald Meyers

Drawings by
Danmark & Michaels

POPULAR SCIENCE

HARPER & ROW

New York, Evanston, San Francisco, London

3/12/82, Sci, B+t, $3.56

Library of Congress Catalog Card Number: 77-26478
ISBN: 06-0906480

Manufactured in the United States of America

Contents

Preface

When Popular Science Books asked me to do a book on insulation and other energy-savers in the home, I was pretty busy doing other things. But I was also reading the newspapers. It was clear to me that the United States was mortgaging its future to the OPEC nations by continuing to be the most wasteful country (by far) in its energy consumption. Spiraling oil imports were having a devastating effect on our economy, our safety, indeed, our very existence.

But no one was listening. The "moral equivalent of war," as the energy crisis was described by President Carter, was being lost by attrition in the battlefields of Congress, where today's votes were more important than the children of tomorrow.

There isn't much we can do about Congress, but there's a lot we can do about the energy problem. If this book inspires a few thousand families to each save a few gallons of oil, a couple of therms of gas, or a watt or two of electricity, then maybe I can say that I did my bit, however small, toward the "war" effort.

Home weatherization is not only good for the nation, it's good for you, too. The energy you save by completing these projects is also money in your pocket. The more energy-efficient your home (or car, boat or whatever) becomes, the less you spend on increasingly expensive oil, gas, or electricity.

I'd like to take this opportunity to thank some of the organizations that assisted me in the preparation of this book. The National Mineral Wool Association and its members, particularly Owens-Corning Fiberglas, deserve a special mention. Thanks also to Dow Chemical, Reynolds Metals Co., Plaskolite, Thermwell Products, the Long Island Lighting Co., Long Island Conservation and Comfort, and the U.S. Department of Energy. A personal thanks to John Miracola, Bernie Frisse Jr., and Kenny Mann for "modeling."

A special thank you to Condé, who crawled around in my attic snapping pictures. Last, but not least, to my daughter Cindy, who transcribed my sloppy manuscript into something more legible.

L. Donald Meyers
Shoreham, N.Y.

1 | What Happened?

WHAT IS ALL THIS TO-DO about home energy saving? Our parents never worried about insulation, weatherstrippping, or caulking. Sure, they grumbled about fuel bills, but they grumbled about a lot of things. If they took any action, though, it was probably in the form of a complaint to the coal man. Did you ever see your father (or grandfather) go up in the attic to check his insulation? It's doubtful, because there probably wasn't any.

So what happened? Why is everyone now talking R-factors—whatever they are—and turning down thermostats so that they have to wear sweaters around the house?

It all started with a war far across the seas, a war over a relatively small plot of ground in the Middle East. If you favor one side, you call it Palestine. If you're on the other side, you call it Israel.

Grandpa's attic never looked like this. Here, two layers of R-19 (6″) blanket fiberglass are crisscrossed to provide R-38 (12″) ceiling insulation.

One of the numerous battles over Palestine/Israel began on Yom Kippur in 1973. The Israelis were taken by surprise and lost at first. Then they started to come back, and the Arab countries decided to use a weapon which took the western world by surprise—an economic boycott. The Arab countries refused to ship any oil to the countries which were helping Israel. For months, chaos ensued. Americans, used to plentiful supplies of gasoline, lined up at gas pumps to purchase a measly couple of gallons.

Eventually, the war ended in a shaky truce, and oil supplies were resumed. But the lesson of the boycott was not lost on the oil-producing countries. When they began supplying us with oil again, prices were raised drastically. Within a few months, prices were *quadrupled*. Western nations began to realize how dependent they were on oil when it cost four times as much.

Over the preceding decades, Grandpa's coal furnace had been converted to cheaper, cleaner oil and natural gas. Many homes were heated with electricity, which was heavily dependent on oil-generated utility plants. From 1950 to 1970, the real cost of energy in the U.S. decreased 28 percent.

Now, suddenly, the "cheaper" oil, gas, and electric heating units were costing us a lot more money. The government became anxious—as well it should have —about what would happen if we were suddenly cut off from Middle Eastern oil again. Not only would we freeze at home. Our airplanes, tanks, and aircraft carriers would be useless.

In-depth studies have shown that, even assuming new oil discoveries and increased production, oil demand will exceed world supplies by about 1990. Estimated reserves will be totally exhausted somewhere from 2010 to 2020.

And so began the big push for "Project Independence" (from foreign oil) in the middle 1970s. This particular program was an acknowledged failure, but President Carter made energy conservation the primary domestic goal of his administration. The Carter program was designed to force us to conserve energy by a carrot-and-stick approach. Rewards were to be offered for saving energy with financial incentives such as tax credits. We'd also be punished for wasting energy with gas-guzzling cars. There were a lot of other rewards and punishments for industry and individuals, but much of the program expired in Congress.

Nonetheless, some of the President's main objectives are in sight. Perhaps the most important achievement was focusing our attention on the problem, and making believers out of many of us who hadn't taken the crisis seriously.

For homeowners, there is one personal "plus" in the package if approved by Congress—a tax credit for those who invest in energy-saving materials for the home. In the long run, however, a more vital achievement may be the realization by most Americans that energy-saving is essential to our country as a whole and to each of us as individuals. President Carter called responding to the energy crisis the "moral equivalent of war." This made most of us stop and think.

Most Americans will do what they can in time of war, whether a shooting or moral war. But energy conservation makes sense in a selfish way as well. It saves money. Turning down the thermostat a couple of degrees can save 5-10 percent in fuel costs over the year. Insulation can save 20-70 percent of fuel costs per year, not counting any tax credit. Making your home truly energy-efficient can save hundreds of dollars annually and can pay back the initial cost in just a few years. Shutting off thermal leaks also pays in comfort and improved health. So it pays, literally, to be a patriot.

Most of us know that older homes are cold and drafty. Few homes built before World War II had any insulation. Fuel costs then were very low. But how about houses built within the past ten years or so? Builders have been aware of rising heating and cooling costs for some years now—but builders are not philanthropists. They put in insulation only when required by building codes. Only a very conscientious builder—and there are some—would increase the cost of a new home by putting in more insulation than he had to. Even in the earlier 1970s, energy costs were far lower. None of us—builder, town inspector, or buyer—paid too much mind to the size, type, and quality of the insulation. Caulk and weatherstripping were installed casually, if at all.

It's a new ballgame now. If you think energy costs are high now, wait till next year—and the year after. Barring an unforeseen miracle, prices will continue to rise inexorably. Every "R" of insulation, every inch of weatherstripping or tube of caulk, will mean dollars saved in the future. Few of us are now unaware of our fuel and electric bills. We can and should find ways to reduce them.

SOME BROAD ECONOMIC EFFECTS. Most of us don't need any more motivation for making our homes more energy-efficient than those already mentioned. Energy conservation is essential to keep our country strong, and it also saves us money. But the energy crunch has other ramifications that affect us in other ways—some more obvious than others.

If you remember the gasoline shortage of 1973–74, you may also recall the inconvenience and wasted hours spent trying to find a few gallons to get to work or to Grandma's house (the one without the insulation). There were plenty of ruined vacations during that time also.

Translate the lost man-hours simply hunting for gas into dollars lost in production, and lost leisure time, and it's obvious that there were serious economic losses, too. Industries that depend on cheap travel were devastated that winter. Sales of recreational vehicles plummeted. Tourism suffered greatly. The whole state of Florida was in economic shock.

And how about the natural-gas shortage during the severe winter of 1976–77? Many industrial plants were shut down, with thousands of workers laid off. Schools were closed, forcing working mothers to leave their jobs or hire sitters. In all parts of the country, people were spending disposable income on much higher fuel bills. That meant fewer movies, meals out, etc.

As of this writing, fuel supplies are adequate, if not plentiful, except for scarce natural gas. But does this mean the energy shortage is over? It does not. We are importing foreign, more costly, oil at a rate of close to $120 million worth a day. The United States grew and prospered during its first two centuries because of a wealth of natural resources. When we have to import these resources, every product which depends on them rises in price. As domestic sources became depleted, more and more foreign oil must be imported, thus pushing the cost of many important products higher and higher. Result—continued high inflation. The cost of foreign oil is one of the most significant factors in this high inflation rate.

All of us wonder why we have been caught so long in economic "stagflation," that deadly mixture of high unemployment plus rising prices. In the Great Depression, unemployment was much worse than it is now, but at least prices came down. In the middle 1970s, our unemployment rate approached that of the 1930s, but prices continued to rise. One of the many complex reasons for this is the fact that we are leaning even more heavily on imported resources such as oil. There was no recession in the oil-producing nations. The monopolistic oil cartel has no competition. Therefore, those countries continued to raise their prices.

It is doubtful that even professional economists, those practitioners of "the dismal science," understand all the causes and effects of our current financial woes, but it means a continued drain on the American dollar, and a weakening of our currency in comparison to other nations. Trade deficits—more money flowing out of a country than into it—depress local industries and cause further unemployment.

Which brings us back to you again, patient reader, and your fuel-guzzling house. It will pay you—in direct dollars and cents in your pocket—to tighten up your home with insulation, weatherstripping, caulking, and the other measures discussed in this book. It will help keep our nation strong if you contribute in only a small way toward conserving our dwindling energy resources. Militarily, this will "keep 'em flying"—and rolling and sailing. Perhaps even more important, it will help preserve America (as well as Europe, Japan, and other fuel-poor countries) from economic distress caused by expensive and ever-increasing fuel imports.

If some of the tasks described in this book become a little difficult, tedious, or boring, it may help to imagine the pleasant surprises in your next fuel bill, a tax credit next April, or next summer's auto trip to the Grand Canyon. You, in your small way, will be responsible for making it all possible. If none of us rises to the task, there may someday be no auto trips for anyone. Our economic well-being is at stake. You can feel good about doing your part. So grab that staple gun, lift that hammer, and join the fray.

2 | You Can Cut Down on Thermal Loss

ABOUT 22 PERCENT of the energy used in the United States is consumed in the residential sector. Private automobiles account for another 15 percent of all the energy used in this country. Thus U.S. citizens burn about 37 percent of all our energy used overall.

Industry, commerce, and agriculture use a lot of energy, too, and pressure has been put upon these sectors to consume less. But we as individuals can do our part as well. If we can convince the rest of the world that we are serious about reducing our consumption and hence our oil imports, it is certain to be a boost for the economy and the American dollar.

But altruism isn't the only motive. We can help ourselves, too, by taking measures toward weatherization of our homes. Virtually every homeowner can cut his fuel costs by at least 10 to 20 percent by one or more of the methods shown in this book. Savings up to 50 percent and even 70 percent are not uncommon in older homes with no insulation and poor weatherstripping and caulking.

Here are some actual cases documented by *Changing Times* magazine:

James P. Dickey of Danbury, Connecticut, uses oil heat. He added 3 inches of insulation to the attic and weatherstripped his doors and windows. The cost of materials was about $300. He lowered his oil consumption by 20 percent the next year, and at current fuel prices he figures to recover his $300 investment in 2.2 years.

Mr. and Mrs. Harry T. Woods are a retired couple in Topeka, Kansas. They have a small one-story brick-and-stucco house heated by natural gas. They invested $100 in additional weatherstripping, two storm doors, and four storm windows. Their gas consumption dropped by 28 percent, and their "payback" period (time required to recoup the $100 investment) is 3.5 years.

Arthur O. Plummer owns a rambling brick ranch—the least energy-efficient type of house—in Rockville, Maryland. He added 3 inches of insulation to his walls, plus 3½ to 4 inches in the attic. He also bought storm windows and doors. In addition, he changed to a "clock-thermostat" which automatically lowers his thermostat from 70°F during the day to 60°F at night. The entire investment was $400, which brought about a 26 percent reduction in his natural-gas consumption for a payback period of 7.5 years.

The homes described above are typical homes, and the savings were accomplished without trying to make these homes super-weathertight. Such an attempt *was* made by the National Bureau of Standards (NBS) to a 22-year-old house in Gaithersburg, Maryland. The 1,054-square-foot house used 881 gallons of

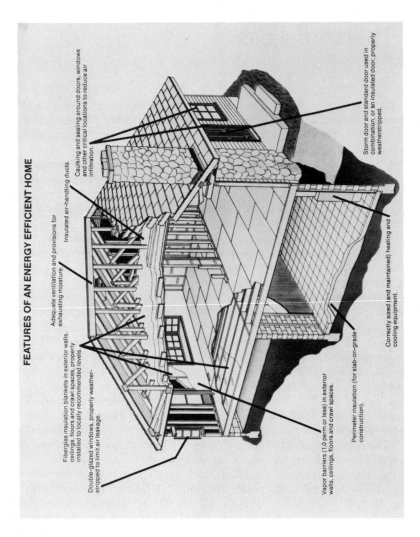

FEATURES OF AN ENERGY EFFICIENT HOME

Adequate ventilation and provisions for exhausting moisture.

Insulated air-handling ducts.

Caulking and sealing around doors, windows and other critical locations to reduce air infiltration.

Storm door and standard door used in combination, or an insulated door, properly weatherstripped.

Fiberglas insulation blankets in exterior walls, ceilings, floors and crawl spaces, properly installed to locally recommended levels.

Double-glazed windows, properly weather-stripped to limit air leakage.

Vapor barriers (1.0 perm or less) in exterior walls, ceilings, floors and crawl spaces.

Perimeter insulation (for slab-on-grade construction).

Correctly sized (and maintained) heating and cooling equipment.

This cutaway drawing by Owens-Corning Fiberglas shows some of the most important energy-saving features in the home.

oil and had 3½ inches of insulation in the attic already. The house was already well weatherstripped. Various tightening-up techniques brought a 52 percent reduction in oil consumption. The oil bill went from $317 one year to $143 the next.

How was it done? Storm doors and windows were purchased for $780, covering about 16 percent of the area of the house, which is average. The energy saving here was computed at 24 percent. Insulation was blown into the wall cavities at a cost of $840, and 5½ more inches were blown on top of the 3½ inches in the attic for $550. Six-inch batts were installed under the floor, and a plastic moisture barrier was laid over the ground in the crawl space. These items cost an additional $360. Total cost—$2530.

Sounds like a lot, huh? It is, but this was all done by a contractor, raising the cost considerably. The investment payback was figured at 13 years for electric heat, 25 for gas, and 26 for oil. Not exactly a dollar-wise investment, which illustrates the pitfalls of plunging into a weatherization program without examining all of the ramifications. Most of the work in this book can be done by the homeowner, which usually results in a substantial savings. We'll help you sort out the good from the bad deals in Chapters 4 and 5.

Owens-Corning Fiberglas Corporation, one of the largest manufacturers of insulation, conducted a computer analysis of the actual annual dollar savings resulting from insulating an attic in a typical small three-bedroom house of 1370 square feet. The table, reproduced on the next page, gives the figures for most major cities in the U.S. and assumes no previous attic insulation. The projected savings are at April 1977 prices. All figures assume electric cooling during the hot months. The left-hand column gives the manufacturer's recommended level of attic insulation for each city in R-values. (A complete discussion of R-values follows in Chapter 4. But, R-19 means 6 inches of fiberglass.)

You can determine the recommended R-value for attics in your area by finding the city nearest you and checking the left-hand column. To get an idea as to what you might save by putting the recommended insulation in an uninsulated attic, look under the column for your type of heating system. If your house is

The insulating tasks in an unfinished attic can be done by the average do-it-yourselfer. One of the easiest and most cost-effective tasks is to add new insulation to the old insulation.

ANNUAL DOLLAR SAVINGS FROM ATTIC INSULATION

CITY	R-VALUE	GAS HEAT, ELECTRIC A/C	OIL HEAT, ELECTRIC A/C	ELECTRIC HEAT AND A/C	HEAT PUMP HEAT AND A/C
Albany, N. Y.	33	288	364	679	366
Albuquerque	33	158	272	427	230
Atlanta	26	127	211	276	155
Bakersfield, Calif.	26	145	207	304	177
Birmingham	26	154	245	364	216
Bismarck, N. D.	38	211	442	491	284
Boise, Ida.	33	279	320	298	149
Boston	33	305	332	582	298
Buffalo	33	235	355	666	352
Burlington, Vt.	38	420	445	819	456
Casper, Wyo.	33	195	381	446	242
Charleston, S. C.	26	132	192	262	155
Charleston, W. Va.	30	181	261	390	208
Charlotte	26	198	231	316	170
Chattanooga	26	134	224	257	142
Chicago	33	222	336	422	241
Cincinnati	30	207	273	405	217
Cleveland	33	210	305	450	240
Columbus, Ohio	30	218	296	459	249
Corpus Christi	26	246	251	374	266
Dallas	26	234	276	420	275
Denver	33	134	320	442	236
Des Moines	33	203	326	576	331
Detroit	33	232	333	767	411
El Paso	26	160	223	335	196
Ft. Wayne	33	210	314	476	257
Fresno	26	143	209	321	176
Grand Rapids, Mich.	33	236	347	696	375
Great Falls, Mont.	38	204	377	373	196
Harrisburg	30	288	302	530	276
Hartford	33	284	351	705	376
Houston	26	129	156	198	127
Indianapolis	30	198	288	308	167
Jackson, Miss.	26	157	220	324	193
Jacksonville	26	167	198	313	202
Kansas City, Mo.	30	173	284	399	227
Knoxville	26	153	221	242	129
Las Vegas	26	170	237	311	190
Little Rock	26	240	334	686	412
Los Angeles	19	80	156	286	132

Louisville	30	152	276	390	212
Lubbock, Tex.	26	176	263	409	240
Memphis	26	115	216	234	134
Miami	26	127	127	127	127
Milwaukee	33	256	346	554	302
Minneapolis	38	238	387	477	282
Mobile	26	180	224	327	213
Nashville	26	149	229	263	147
New Orleans	26	144	175	277	173
New York	30	399	350	1014	529
Oklahoma City	26	179	260	316	192
Omaha	33	178	322	434	253
Philadelphia	30	281	322	544	299
Phoenix	26	207	266	303	223
Pittsburgh	33	238	330	464	248
Portland, Me.	33	526	409	668	352
Portland, Ore.	19	199	246	366	166
Raleigh	26	190	234	310	171
Reno	33	285	357	836	438
Richmond	30	233	280	409	231
Sacramento	30	116	190	110	62
Salt Lake City	30	162	334	415	222
San Antonio	26	225	253	369	252
San Francisco	19	134	209	444	183
Seattle	19	229	276	182	81
Shreveport, La.	26	122	190	226	143
Sioux Falls, S. D.	33	286	466	734	419
St. Louis	30	243	303	325	204
Syracuse	33	275	346	643	346
Tampa	26	132	144	199	139
Waco, Tex.	26	220	251	303	213
Washington, D. C.	30	255	308	532	289
Wichita, Kans.	30	178	296	356	216

similar to the 1370-square-foot ranch, the figures should be close. For larger and smaller one-story homes, there should be proportionate savings. Savings for two-story homes, split-levels, etc. are more difficult to compute, but you can get a general idea by comparing the figures.

If you live in or near Denver, for example, and own a home like the one in the study, your attic should be insulated up to R-33 (about 9¼ inches of mineral-wool blankets). With natural-gas heating, you should save $134 in fuel and electric bills per year. With fuel oil, you will save $320, electric heat $442, and a fuel pump $236. For other size homes, take a percentage by comparing square footage. If you have a 2000-square-foot home, for example, you should save about 1½ times as much. Remember, though, that the savings shown are based on April 1977 utility bills in that particular city, and prices may vary widely in surrounding communities. The huge annual savings in New York City for electric heat, for example, is possible because New York has very high electric bills. In neighboring New Jersey, Connecticut, and Long Island, the prices are lower, so the savings will be less.

These examples are only meant to give you a rough idea of the potential savings—to whet your appetite, so to speak. And, remember, this is for the insulation only. It is possible to make more precise calculations as illustrated in Chapters 4 and 5.

INSPECTING YOUR ATTIC. By now, we trust that you are at least theoretically convinced that energy and dollars can be saved in most homes. But how about yours? There's one way to find out. Let's take a look, beginning in the attic. As you make your inspection, make notes and use graph paper to make sketches of which areas need "weatherization."

If you have an older home, there may be stairs and a door to the attic. If so, simply take a walk up there. It is more usual in houses built after World War II, however, to have an access trap or "scuttle" door. The builder has probably left a hole in the ceiling, surrounded by molding and covered by a scrap of plywood or paneling painted to match the ceiling. More often than not, this is located in an obscure closet area.

Getting up through the access hole may be difficult, especially if you're getting a little creaky in the joints. A short straight ladder or longer stepladder is ordinarily necessary. Even so, you may wind up having to pull yourself up between the joists (wooden ceiling beams).

Make sure that the ladder is securely braced, or have someone keep his feet on the legs while you crawl up. As you lift the trap door, you will undoubtedly find your first energy waster. Even in well-insulated attics, it will be unusual to find the trap cover insulated. The scuttle-hole cover in my home was a ¼-inch-thick scrap of paneling. Lots of heat is lost through that thin piece of wood. The R-factor of ¼-inch plywood paneling is .25—which is almost like having nothing at all.

In any case, assume that somehow you've raised your body into the attic area. The first thing to check (if you haven't before) is whether or not there is any type of flooring up there. If not, be careful where you stand. What may look like solid footing on the underside of the joists is simply the back side of the ceiling material below. Even if you're a real featherweight, don't step on this. You may go right through to the floor below. At best, you'll have a gaping hole in the ceiling which won't be easy to patch.

If there aren't any boards at all to stand on, you'll need to bring up a wood plank or a piece of plywood. Lay your board across the wood joists, preferably with the ends just slightly over the edge of the joists. Another common attic accident is stepping on the end of a loose board and tumbling through the ceiling.

Set the board down carefully as discussed, usually while sitting on the open

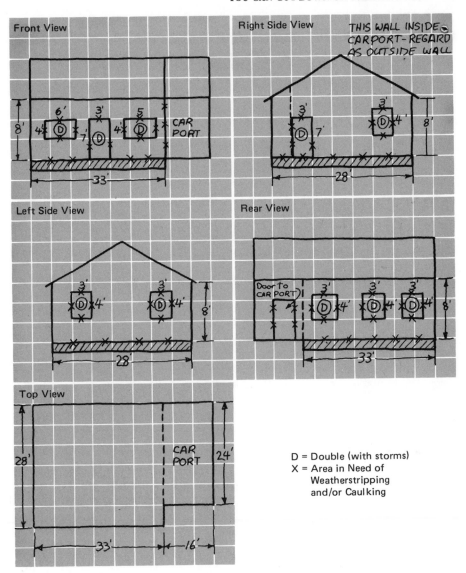

Use graph paper as shown here to make rough drawings of what your house looks like. Make notations on the drawings as to where you need insulation and other weatherproofing.

joists adjoining the trap hole. Now stand, crouch, or kneel on this while you inspect the insulation, if any. If there isn't any insulation, you still haven't wasted your time by climbing up there, because there are a few other things to check, as explained later.

This uninsulated attic area shows bare wallboard for the ceiling below. A lot of heat is lost in this case.

If there is insulation up there, pull up on a piece. If it's stapled to the joists, rip off a few of them. It won't hurt anything. Look around for an R-number somewhere on the underside. It should either be marked in small print on the flanges or printed large on the foil or kraft-paper vapor barrier. If there is no vapor barrier, and all you're looking at is the same woolly stuff that's on the other side, you may have two problems. First, you'll have no accurate way to judge the effectiveness of what's there. Second, you may have to provide a vapor barrier. If none is attached to the insulation, perhaps the builder used foil-faced gypsum board, which will serve the same purpose. Or there may be a sheet of plastic under the insulation, which also serves as a vapor barrier. Check below the insulation for either of these before concluding that you'll have to put in a new vapor barrier.

It is probable that older insulation will not have the R-number clearly marked. Or you could have poured, loose insulation. In such cases, note the number of inches. Take a measurement in some part where it isn't matted down or pulled apart. Convert inches to R-value by using the table here.

R-VALUES FOR VARIOUS THICKNESSES OF INSULATION

	BATTS OR BLANKETS		LOOSE FILL (POURED IN)			
	Glass Fiber	Rock Wool	Glass Fiber	Rock Wool	Cellulosic Fiber	
R-7	2″	1¾″	3½″	3″	1¾″	R-7
R-11	3½″-4″	3″	5″	4″	3″	R-11
R-13	4″	3½″	6″	4½″	3½″	R-13
R-19	6″-6½″	5¼″	8″-9″	6″-7″	5″	R-19
R-22	6½″	6″	10″	7″-8″	6″	R-22
R-26	8″	7½″	12″	9″	7″-7½″	R-26
R-30	9½″-10½″	9″	13″-14″	10″-11″	8″	R-30
R-33	11″	10″	15″	11″-12″	9″	R-33
R-38	12″-13″	10½″	17″-18″	13″-14″	10″-11″	R-38

While in the attic, check the ventilation system. Note the number and size of vents on the sidewalls near the peak or the soffits (underside of the eaves).

Are there any attic fans or "caps" in the roof? Just note the number and approximate size for now. More on this in Chapter 13.

The condition of the insulation is important, too. Insulating materials are almost indestructible, but a number of things can go wrong. It can be poorly installed, with gaps, tears, and places where the insulation was not fitted properly around plumbing, wiring, and other obstructions. Leaks in the roof can mat down the insulation, rendering it virtually useless. If that is the case, make a notation with a big check mark to have the roof repaired.

Floored and finished attics. Attics that are used often for storage will probably be floored. If the floor is simply a convenience for walking, with cheap or loose boards, pull up a few and check as above. If the attic is used for living space, with hardwood or tile floors, you won't want to mess with the flooring unless you have an insatiable curiosity. It makes no difference, anyway, because this type of attic needs insulation above, not below.

Chapter 7 gives details on how to check for insulation in finished attics, but you may already have noticed that the attic rooms are terribly hot in the summer and quite cold in the winter. If not, and it's reasonably chilly outside, put one hand on an outside wall. If it's cold to the touch, you need insulation. To verify this, put one hand on the outside wall and another on an inside partition. When there's a difference, you need insulation. See Chapter 7 for ways of getting behind the finishing materials for a look at what's behind them.

Before you leave the attic. There is one more thing to look at before you leave the attic. Some older homes were framed with "balloon" construction. In this type of construction, the outside studs extend the full height of the building, without plates at each floor level. If so, you can look down the stud cavities to see if there's any insulation there. This also means that you can pour insulation down between the studs yourself, saving a lot of money on contractor's costs.

TESTING THE WALLS. After you leave the attic, perform the hand test as described above for the outside walls of the house. When the weather's too warm for this, remove an electrical outlet cover and see if you can see into the stud area. A flashlight will assist here, but be sure to turn the current off at the electrical entrance panel before getting too close to the wiring. When all else fails, chip away a little of the drywall or plaster to get a good look.

If, as expected, the insulation is below standard, make a note of whatever you do have and consult Chapters 4 and 8 to determine the desirability of doing anything about it. It may be that adding insulation here will be a poor investment. The only reasonable way to insulate these walls is by having a contractor blow in the insulating material, and this is usually the least cost-effective insulating job in your home.

CHECKING THE BASEMENT. The last stop on your interior inspection tour is the basement, if you have one. A common and understandable misconception is that concrete makes a good insulator. The basement is usually cooler in the summer and warmer in the winter than the outside air, so we conclude that it's because of the concrete. But is it true?

Emphatically, no. Concrete is a notoriously poor insulator, with an R-value of only .08 per inch. A typical 8-inch concrete foundation wall has an R-value of only .64, about the same as a sheet of ½-inch plywood (.63).

The reason that basements feel cooler in summer and warmer in winter is that they are mostly underground. Earth, at least below the frost level, is a fairly constant 55°F. Most heating units are located in the basement, and they waste enough heat to keep the nearby area relatively warm. Anyone who owns a "raised-ranch" home, where the lower level is high off the ground, knows how cold concrete can be.

There are several things to look for in your basement. First, check for insulation. If it's a finished basement, the odds are high that there is no insulation. Some don't need it. But most do, so try to find out by using one of the wall tests above. If the basement's unfinished, the job is easy. One quick look will establish whether any insulation exists. There may be insulation under the flooring above. In fact, there *should* be if any part of the basement is used for outside access, such as a garage. Most building codes require it. Such insulation should be covered with gypsum wallboard, also required in most codes. You can assume that a basement garage is insulated if the ceiling is covered with drywall, but usually this type of job is sloppy enough so that you can see through holes or around the edges to check. Chances are good that such insulation is skimpy at best.

The "band joists" are the outside joists that rest on the horizontal wood bottom plate above the concrete. These are rarely insulated, and they should be. Make a note of it.

If the flooring above the basement is insulated between the joists, there is generally no need to insulate the basement walls unless you use the basement (or plan to) for living space. In that event, consider insulating the basement walls, at least 2 feet below the level of earth around it. In any case, take notes for later use.

It is important while in the basement to check all the openings to the outside. All pipes, wiring, etc. leading outside should be packed with insulation. When the basement is not used for living quarters, insulation should be stuffed into the spaces where water pipes and wiring go through to the upper floors. It is also wise to have insulation all along both cold- and hot-water pipes. Insulation keeps heat inside hot-water pipes, and prevents cold-water pipes from sweating. Piping or ducts from the heating unit also benefit from insulation. Is there insulation around the hot-water tank? Check weatherstripping on all doors leading outside and upstairs. Again, make notes.

CRAWL SPACES AND CONCRETE SLABS. Crawl spaces are even more fun to inspect than attics. You will undoubtedly have to get down on your hands and knees after you find a way to get in there. That's why they call it a crawl space. If the ground under the crawl space isn't properly covered with a moisture barrier, you may well have to crawl on some wet, soggy ground. Bring along a board or plank to kneel on.

Crawl spaces are insulated in two ways. Sometimes the floors above have blanket insulation between the joists. Usually, however, there is thick polyethylene sheeting spread over the ground with insulation along the walls. The moisture barrier is sometimes black, but may be transparent, so don't just look in and conclude there's nothing there. In addition to the moisture barrier, blankets or batts should be laid along the band joists and the foundation walls, extending about 2 feet onto the moisture barrier on the ground. If there's nothing there, you have work to do.

There's no way of telling if a concrete slab has been properly insulated. The builder should have used rigid foam insulation on the inside of the footings, between them and the slab itself. You can't see it. If you have a slab, and the floors feel cold, it is very possible insulation is needed. If your home was built just after World War II, as many slab homes were, rigid foam didn't exist then. You can't now insulate the slab the way it should've been done to begin with, but there are measures you can take, as explained in Chapter 9. For now, just make a note that it should be done.

CHECKING OUTSIDE. Now that you've noted the thermal insufficiencies inside of your home, it's time to check the exterior and openings such as windows and doors. There are several important elements to note here. The most efficient way of doing this is by using rough sketches of each elevation and making notations as you go along.

First, sketch in all the openings such as windows and doors. It's better if you measure, but not absolutely necessary. You can "eyeball" the upstairs window measurements, for example, by measuring one or two downstairs windows and making comparisons.

Begin your survey by noting which of the windows have storm sash. Storm windows are one of the effective ways of preventing thermal loss. Storm doors help, too, but not as much as storm windows. If any of the windows are already double-paned with "Thermopane" or similar-type windows, make a note of that also. Also record any other windows which are not the usual double-hung sash. Casement, sliding, and louvered windows fall into this category.

Other important aspects of your exterior inspection are caulking and weather-stripping.

Caulking. Caulk (sometimes spelled "calk") is a flexible material similar to spackling or glazing compound. It is used to seal cracks and other openings in the house and is usually applied in a caulking gun. The gun is an inexpensive instrument which can be purchased for under $2. The compound comes in a cartridge or tube which is inserted into the gun. There are several different types, but more on this in Chapter 11.

For the moment, all you have to know is that the exterior of your home should have caulking wherever two surfaces meet, and in any other places where heat can escape or drafts can come into the house. Some of the places where caulking should be applied are around door and window trim, where pipes and wiring go through the exterior finishing material, around chimneys, and wherever two different materials come together.

Caulk is sometimes used inside as well, but usually for other purposes than to plug up thermal loss. To make your inspection, start at the bottom of the outside of your house, above the foundation, and check the underside of the first row of shingles or clapboard. There should be no gaps there. If there is caulking

The open area around the oil fill pipe is a favorite escape hatch for expensive heat. Caulking seals the leak.

there already, note its condition. Press with your fingers and see if it crumbles and falls off. If it does either, the old caulk should be scraped off and new material applied.

Now walk around the house and check all the spaces around the door and window trim. You may have been fortunate enough to have had a carpenter who set all the siding exactly flush and tight to the trim, but this is not too likely. If there is any space at all, caulking is necessary. Here, as elsewhere, check the condition of any old caulk. Make notes on where the job needs doing. If you have storm windows, they should have been caulked when installed, but check condition (see Chapter 12).

As you make your exterior tour of the doors and windows, note any other openings as you go by. Watch for exterior faucets, electrical wiring, oil-fill pipes, holes for antennas and cables, large cracks between siding and shingles, dryer vents, and all other openings which allow thermal loss. Caulking often fails between the bricks of the chimney and the wood siding because of the different expansion rates.

Don't forget the second story, and dormers and gables. Look for the same caulking areas there. You'll need a sturdy ladder, of course. Unheated attic areas do not need caulking, but anything below the attic insulation does.

It may help to make rough estimates of the number of linear feet that need caulking. It is difficult to get an accurate reading of how many tubes of caulk you will need, but some guidelines are helpful. If you have a good eye for short distances, take a stab at putting down the width of each crack and opening. That will also help later in your estimates, but it isn't worth the time and effort to measure each opening. It's easier to order more caulk than you need and take the leftovers back.

Weatherstripping. It should be obvious, but we'll say it anyway: Don't caulk around window sash or under doors. One enterprising how-to writer (who shall be nameless) was so busy caulking all the cracks be could find that he caulked

16

under the storm door. His wife came out to check his progress and was rewarded with a footfull of caulk.

Openings around all doors proper (as opposed to sills, jambs, and drip caps) are sealed with weatherstripping. This comes in many forms, which are described in Chapter 10. On your inspection tour, all you have to know is that all four sides of each exterior door should contain some kind of material which is designed to seal the gaps when the door is closed. Look for strips of felt, sponge rubber, vinyl, or flexible metal along the top and sides of each door. The bottom of the door should be fitted with a threshold which butts tightly against the door bottom or contains flexible material that does. The best outside doors have interlocking metal channels which seal off the air. You may find the front door well weatherstripped, while other doors are often skipped or equipped with flimsy material. A frequent source of heat loss and drafts is the door to an unheated basement. Perhaps you or an earlier owner installed a "sweep," a piece of swing-out rubber or vinyl that slides along the rug. This is better than nothing, but for a weathertight door, make a note to install something better.

Windows can be a little tricky to evaluate. Often what seems like a draft from poor weatherstripping is actually cold air through the framing caused by a lack of insulation. Windows are usually installed in a precut frame opening with a little room to spare for adjustments. These openings should have been filled with insulation once the windows were in, but often weren't. (The same holds true for doors.) The only way to check this is by removing the trim around the windows. This can be a tedious job calling for refinishing the trim. It's usually not worth the effort.

Newer windows often have factory-installed weatherstripping. Very common are the combination spring-metal slides that spring in and out to hold the windows up and down. These also serve as weatherstripping. But note the bottoms of each window, and the space between the top and bottom double-sash windows where they meet. Many windows will benefit from a strip of felt or sponge rubber at the top and bottom. To test the spacing between the two windows, try to slip a piece of paper between them when they're closed. If it goes through easily, a thin piece of weatherstripping will do its bit there toward draft evasion. Also check for broken panes and deteriorated putty.

You will probably find a great need for weatherstripping in older homes, especially if none has ever been done before. Even where it has been done, much of the older weatherstripping was done with felt, which wears easily and needs frequent replacement. Felt weatherstripping is still the biggest seller, in spite of much more durable types on the market. But more of this in Chapter 10.

ATTACHED GARAGES. One often-neglected source of thermal loss is in an attached garage or a garage built into the basement. Builders seem to treat these as they did the old free-standing type. There is little or no weatherstripping in the door that leads to the house, and usually no attempt to weatherstrip the garage doors themselves. Children—even parents—often leave the garage door open on not-too-nippy days, and the thermal loss through the garage is great. In addition to insulation, make sure that the door from the garage to the house or basement is thoroughly weatherstripped. I also recommend weatherstripping

Garage doors without weatherstripping can be a major source of heat loss when the garage is attached to the house.

the garage door, at least on the bottom, and stuffing insulation into the many open or thin areas around the garage doors.

My garage is in the basement of a house located on the side of a hill. The foundation walls are exposed almost to full depth on the west side, and fully exposed on the garage-door side to the north. My office is on the other side of that garage, and it got very cold in the winter. So did the floors above the garage. After I insulated the exposed west wall and weatherstripped the garage doors as well as the door from the garage to the basement, the other side of the basement was much warmer in the cold months. Other techniques helped warm the floor above. See Chapter 9 for details of this.

WHAT NOW? If you found no defects in your insulation, caulking, or weatherstripping, you are a lucky homeowner indeed. As a matter of fact, perhaps you ought to look again. You must have missed something.

But now the good news. Every defect can be remedied, some quite cheaply. Some will cost you. But in the long run, every dollar expended will be returned in the form of lower fuel and utility costs. In Chapter 5, you can determine whether the cost is worth the investment for your own home.

But maybe Christmas is coming up, or college tuition, vacation, your daughter's wedding—it's always something. No matter how much you might eventually save, most of us can't just shell out a couple of hundred, or thousand, on insulation without feeling it.

More good news. Help is available, and at rather generous terms (comparatively, anyway). Federal and many state government regulations have made it easy to borrow. Even the bankers are cooperating. The next chapter gives the details.

Another familiar garage defect: The stop has been grazed by a car and knocked off. Partially warmed air just pours through the open space.

Insulation isn't the whole answer. This book is concerned with preventing heat loss by proper insulating, caulking, and weatherstripping. However, Chapter 13 does go into some detail about other ways of saving energy around your home, and you should be aware that even in a super-insulated home you could be wasting a lot of heat.

For example, it is vitally important to keep your heating unit at peak efficiency. When was the last time yours was tuned up? It should be done once a year. Are all registers open and clear of obstruction?

Fireplaces and wood stoves are discussed briefly in Chapter 13. But do one thing right now. Check to see if your damper is closed when the fireplace isn't in use. Lots of heat is escaping up that chimney if it's open while the furnace is on.

You must have heard by now about lowering your thermostat. If you haven't done it, do so. Also consider installing a clock-thermostat (see Chapter 13). It's an easy way to save lots of money. It will feel uncomfortable for a few days, but you'll get used to it. We used to keep ours at 75° all the time, then lowered it to 72° and eventually down to 68° in the living zone. (My daughters complained when I tried 65°.) Recently we had our rugs cleaned, and kept the heat up for a few days to help dry them. Everyone in the family was sweltering in the 75° that only a few years ago seemed just right. In the sleeping quarters, 65° is plenty warm enough, 60° even better. What are blankets for?

3 | Financing Energy Improvements

IT IS EASY to be convinced that energy-saving improvements are a good investment in the long run. One sticky problem often remains, however—money. Materials are expensive. As this is written, fiberglass insulation costs about twice what it did just a few years ago. The reason for the price increase has to do with the huge surge in demand, inflation, shortages, and higher costs to the manufacturer—plus perhaps, a touch of profiteering. But the fact remains that any home improvement does cost money. No matter how desirable, it can't be done without the capital.

Take heart. There are ways to get the required bread. And there may be government incentives to ease the pain.

FEDERAL AID. For those who are below the poverty level as defined by federal standards, CSA (Community Services Administration) runs a "winterization" program which allows up to $800 in free materials. Another federal agency, CETA (Comprehensive Employment Training Administration), does the actual installation for you—again for nothing. If you are a senior citizen, or think you might fall under the poverty guidelines, contact your local CSA office for details. The guidelines take family size into account and are periodically adjusted; as of January 1, 1978, maximum income for an urban family of four was $7313 and for a rural family of four was $6225.

The CSA winterization program is a nationwide plan readily available in most areas. There are, however, other federal programs which may also be in effect. Most of these require matching funds from each state and/or local municipality, and it is impossible to list all the participants here.

The best place to inquire into the following possibilities is your local Social Service agency. The social worker, however, may not be aware of all of them. If you, your family, or a friend is in financial straits and fuel and utility bills are a major problem, it will be worthwhile to look into these programs.

Department of Health, Education and Welfare (HEW). Under Section 403 of the Social Security Act—Aid to Families with Dependent Children (AFDC)— there are several ways to provide assistance to those who have problems meeting fuel bills, including a $500 grant for winterizing labor or materials. Under the Emergency Assistance Program (EAP), available in more than half the states, funds are available to pay back fuel bills and estimated future bills. These funds are also available to some families who are not now technically eligible for AFDC. Ask the social worker to check 42 U.S.C. 606.

Insulation funds are also available under the Housing Improvement Services (45 C.F.R. 221, 9[b]13).

Department of Housing and Urban Development (HUD). Under the Housing and Community Development Act of 1974, units of local government can provide assistance for insulating and otherwise winterizing homes for low-income families. This must be part of an overall local program, but 100 percent federal aid is potentially available by combining funds under Section 105.

Section 312 of the 1964 Housing Act (42 U.S.C. 1452[b]) allows 20-year loans at a low 3 percent interest rate to rehabilitate property located in urban-renewal or certain other areas. Although designed for low-income families, it is possible that others might also be eligible.

Department of Agriculture. Lower-income families should be aware of the fact that any shelter and utility costs in excess of 30 percent of family income are subtracted from the maximum eligibility income. In other words, where the family income level is nominally more than that allowed for food-stamp eligibility, careful recordkeeping may show that you pay more than 30 percent of your income for mortgage payments or rent combined with electric, oil, and/or gas bills. If so, the amount over 30 percent is deducted from your income, which may put you under the wire to make your family eligible for food stamps.

Department of Labor. This federal agency administers the CETA program mentioned above. The Labor Department provides the manpower to install the insulation and perform other house-tightening procedures for low-income families. CSA provides the materials.

TAX CREDITS. All of us, whether poor or otherwise, should be entitled to a tax credit under the new federal energy bill, assuming Congress has gotten its act together by the time you read this. It is important to recognize that a credit, unlike a deduction, is a direct subtraction from your tax, which is much more of a help than a mere deduction or exemption. A deduction for charity, for example, is lumped together with other deductions before computing your total tax. If you donated $200 to the United Fund, your tax is not reduced at all if you use the standard deduction, or if you are in a low tax bracket.

A tax credit is taken from the final adjusted tax and means much more to those in lower and middle income levels. If you pay an annual tax of $1000 and have four dependents, for example, you took a credit of $35 for each dependent in 1976, a direct saving of $140. Weatherization credits work the same way.

The proposed Energy Act of 1976 allows a credit of 25 percent of the first $4000 spent in energy-saving improvements. With the $1000 adjusted tax mentioned above, you can knock off an additional $800. Assuming the same four dependents, your tax would be only $60. Again, the energy bill is in limbo as this is written, but the credit will probably pass in approximately its original form.

Still, that comes in April (or earlier, if you file sooner). Welcome though it is at that time, it doesn't help raise the money when you need it most—now. Where will that come from?

LOANS. You borrow, of course. But for energy savings, the path is easier than for most improvements. In some areas—New York State, for one—utilities are required by law to provide energy-saving loans to their customers at a lower rate of interest than is available otherwise. Other states provide local tax credits. Arizona and Illinois are two of these.

The best way to determine whether your area provides special loans or credits for energy-saving home improvements is to check local energy agencies, banks, contractors, or insulation dealers.

Many of these utility loans are provided through banks, some directly by the utility itself. The annual interest rate in New York State is limited to the allowed profit for the utility. The Long Island Lighting Company, for example, is limited by law to 9.7 percent net profit, and the rate of interest to you is the same. Loans are made to the extent that the consumer would be able to pay the loan out of what he saved on his heating bills. The projected improvement, in other words, would have to pay for itself within the prescribed seven-year period. Most of the do-it-yourself projects in this book easily meet that requirement. If you hire a contractor, they may or may not pay for themselves in seven years. But the utility figures that out for you.

Loans in New York are a minimum of $200 and a maximum of $1500 for a single-family home. Renters are eligible if the owner approves and other conditions, such as credit-worthiness, are complied with. Many other states have similar standards.

Federally backed low interest rates. There are several ways you can get a low-interest loan because the payment is guaranteed by the federal government if you default.

FmHA (Farmers Home Administration) loans. These are made to those in rural areas, not necessarily farmers, who have been turned down by regular lenders. Loans of up to $2500, payable at 1 percent interest (the rest is subsidized) for up to ten years, are available under Section 504 of the Housing Act of 1949. Larger loans, though rare, are also available for up to 33 years. These loans can be used for insulation or any other winterization program. According to the government, many "suburban" areas are still regarded as "rural," so don't assume that you are not eligible because you don't have cows or grow potatoes.

HUD (Department of Housing and Urban Development) loans. HUD is now the administrator of the old FHA (Federal Housing Authority) loans. Two types of loans are available. If you are making structural changes to your home, such as an addition (which should be insulated), you may qualify for a long-term loan. Most of the jobs in this book, however, will fall under the Title I category. This type of loan is designed for alterations and repairs that "enhance the livability" of the home. Insulation certainly does that. Such loans are made through regular lending institutions and are insured by the FHA. The limit is $10,000, with up to seven years to pay. The interest rate varies with availability of money, but it's usually somewhere between the prevailing mortgage rate and regular loans. FHA insurance costs an extra ½ percent.

Life insurance loans. You can borrow on the cash value of a non-term policy, and this is one of the best and easiest ways to get ready cash. It is possible to borrow up to 95 percent of the value of the policy at a very low rate—perhaps as low as 5 percent. Contact your insurance agent as to exact rates, current cash value, etc.

Credit unions. These are a good source of funds at reasonable interest. Members are usually given loans without too much difficulty. (They know where to find you.) Contrary to a common misconception, you don't usually have to be a member for a long time. If there is a credit union at work, or if you belong to an organization which has one, inquire into joining it. Since credit unions are cooperatives, more or less, any profit that is made goes back to their members. So you can't lose whether you borrow or not.

Open-end mortgages. This type of mortgage allows you to borrow up to the full amount of the principal once a certain amount has been repaid. If, for instance, you took out a $30,000 mortgage on your home and have lived there for some time, the principal may now be down to $25,000. You can now borrow up to $5000 more with few, if any, questions asked. Usually, you must borrow in multiples of $1000. This type of mortgage is not too common any more, but many older ones had this provision. Check the contract, your lawyer, or the bank.

Refinanced mortgages. If you're going heavily into debt for contractor-installed insulation or anything else involving a substantial amount of money, you could refinance your house. This is ordinarily a poor financial deal and probably involves abandoning a low-interest mortgage for a high one. There will also be additional closing costs, although they won't be as high as the original "settlement" costs.

If tax credits and paybacks in fuel savings are great enough, the disadvantages can be outweighed. A refinanced mortgage, however, is usually a last resort for those who can't manage any other way. It may also be the only choice for those who plan on other, more expensive, improvements, such as room additions, in addition to insulating.

Secondary mortgage loans. These are available in most states and are another popular way of borrowing on the increased equity of a home. Interest rates are relatively high, but better than standard loans. Check local loan agencies for details.

Other financing methods. You might try a personal bank loan, a collateral loan (using stocks, bonds, real estate, or other assets), good old Dad, or a rich uncle. Some banks offer a discount on interest rates for energy-saving loans. If you are using a contractor, he may be able to arrange financing for you. This may be quick and convenient, but will probably be the most costly.

DOES IT PAY? If you have to take out an expensive loan to make your home weather-tight, do the interest and other costs offset the savings in fuel and utility bills? That depends, of course, on many things, including the financing cost. In general, most energy improvements will pay off even if you pay a high interest rate, because you will save more than you pay. The only real way to tell, however, is to add the interest cost to the other factors in Chapter 5.

There's more to it than that, though. When you bought your house, chances are that you paid little or no attention to the insulation, weatherstripping, or caulking. Current homebuyers are paying a *lot* of attention to these items. In a very real sense, they add to the resale value of your home. Prospective home-buyers will no doubt want to look at your fuel bills, and will be impressed if you can show that they aren't as bad as elsewhere. That's about the most any-one can ask these days.

Then there's always the intangible value of a warm, draft-free house to con-sider. A well-winterized home feels more comfortable, and you'll be able to sit close to the outside walls once they're well insulated, caulked, and weather-stripped, thus gaining more living space. And at the risk of waving the flag a little too high, I'll add that it's also a good feeling to know that you're con-tributing your bit toward the "war" effort.

So in most cases you'll find that there is an actual dollar savings when you borrow to weathertighten your home. And, even if the figures indicate a net loss, consider the other factors mentioned above before you decide not to do it.

4 | Calculating Energy Losses

CERTAINLY, THE MEDIA have taken a great interest in home weatherizing of late. The energy problem, high fuel costs, and other factors have generated a lot of interest (and high-pressure salesmen). But are insulation, weatherstripping, and caulking good investments? Generally yes, but not always. It all depends on the cost of materials, whether you can do it yourself, and most of all, the payback period. But let's start at the beginning.

To understand why you have heat loss or gain in your home, you should have a basic understanding of what heat flow is and how it works. When the outside and inside temperatures are both 68°, there is no heat transmission. As soon as there is a difference between outside and inside temperatures, heat flow begins. There is movement of the warm air toward the colder air. In the winter, the inside air becomes colder. In summer, it becomes hotter. A constant equalization is at work, wherein the heat keeps flowing toward the cooler section. The greater the temperature difference, the more rapid the flow.

The actual transfer of heat is accomplished in three ways:

Radiation is the emission of energy from an object such as the sun. It travels at the speed of light. This type of heat doesn't concern us much in the home, although it does occur directly around a heating coil or fireplace. Radiated heat travels in straight lines only. For our purposes, the other two forms of heat flow are the important ones.

Convection is the transmission of heat by a liquid or gas. It is the principle by which our heating systems work. Cold air is drawn into the heating unit, heated by the flame, and forced out into our rooms by one method or another. In general, warm air rises and cold air falls, but the molecules of air are churning throughout the entire house, too, so that an overall warming of the whole structure occurs.

Conduction is the flow of heat energy through a solid. In the esoteric world of space travel, materials have been created which reduce this type of heat flow drastically. Certain types of ceramics, mica sheets, and urethane are combined to keep the intense heat of space travel outside the vehicle. But there is no one material or combination thereof that does not have *some* conductivity. Therefore insulation does not *stop* the transfer of heat—it merely slows it down.

All materials in common use for home-building have been tested by the National Bureau of Standards, other laboratories, and manufacturers, so that we can calculate exactly what the conductivity, or heat transfer rate, is for each.

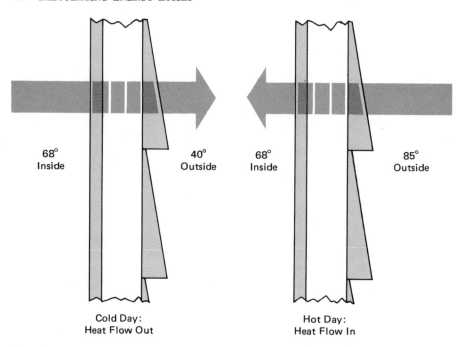

68° Inside	40° Outside	68° Inside	85° Outside

Cold Day:
Heat Flow Out

Hot Day:
Heat Flow In

Heat always flows from the warm to the cold side, regardless of direction. When the temperature is exactly the same on the outside as inside, there is no heat flow.

HOW CONDUCTIVITY IS COMPUTED. When you are calculating your own insulation needs, you will be able to use the table "R-Values of House Components" that appears later in this chapter. However, it will be to your advantage to understand just how R-values are derived. First, though let's consider K, which is a measure of conductivity and the inverse of R.

K is the letter assigned to the rate of heat flow through a material. The K-factor tells you how much heat energy will pass through 1 square foot of a given material in terms of Btu per hour at a 1°F difference in temperature. (Btu means British thermal units, and is an arbitrary standard based on the energy it takes to raise the temperature of 1 pound of water by 1°. Imagine the heat given off by a wooden kitchen match, and you have a rough idea how much 1 Btu is.) Thus the formula for K is:

$$K = \text{Btu/hr./ft.}^2/\text{F}° \quad \text{(heat loss per hour through 1 square foot of a given material at a temperature difference of 1°)}$$

The U-factor of any wall is a combination of the K-factors that make up the wall, also taking into consideration the thicknesses of each material. Note that the air space itself has its own K-value, as does the film of air on the outside and inside of the wall. Thus the formula for U is:

$$U = \cfrac{1}{\dfrac{\text{thickness of A}}{\text{K factor of A}} + \dfrac{\text{thickness of B}}{\text{K factor of B}} + \dfrac{\text{thickness of C}}{\text{K factor of C}}, \text{etc.}}$$

The R-factor is the one that we will be most concerned with in this book. The R-factor is simply the inverse of the K and U factors. While K and U represent the thermal *transfer* of certain materials, R represents the thermal *impedance*—that is, the *resistance* of that material to heat transfer. When applied to an entire wall, the R-value means the capacity of that wall to contain the heat on either side. The formula for R, in terms of U, is very simple:

$$R = \frac{1}{U} \text{ or } U = \frac{1}{R} \text{ (R is the inverse of U)}$$

We have discussed R-factors in a general way already in this book. You have seen that the higher the R-factor, the better the insulation. (Conversely, the higher the K-factor or U-factor, the greater the heat loss.) In more technical terms, the higher the R-factor, the better the capacity of the wall, ceiling, or whatever to resist the flow of heat molecules from the warm side to the cool side.

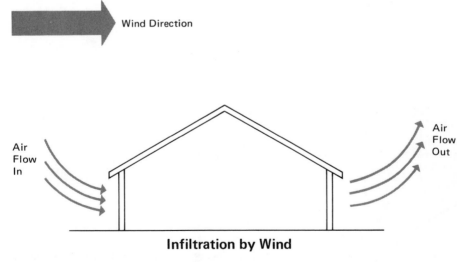

Infiltration by Wind

Heat flow is accelerated by the action of winds, which force cold air in, and warm air out, by infiltration.

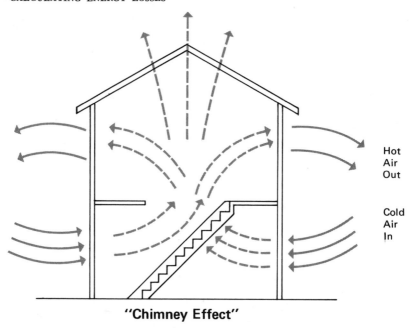

"Chimney Effect"

Because of the chimney effect, warm air tends to escape through the top of the house, drawing in more cold air at the bottom of the house.

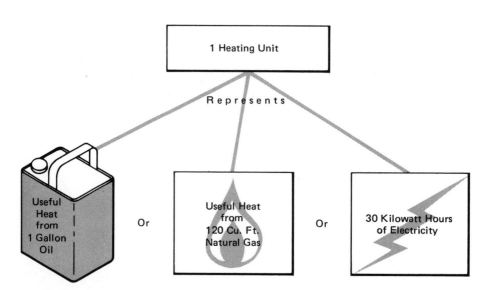

A heating unit, as defined by the Dept. of Energy, represents the equivalent amount of useful heat from 1 gallon of heating oil, 120 cubic feet of natural gas, or 30 kilowatts of electricity.

AIR INFILTRATION. Suppose that your home is fully insulated, so that the R-factors of the entire home are as high as or higher than needed. Will that cut down on heating bills? Yes, it will, but it's only part of the story.

Warm air will normally leak out through the cracks, chinks, holes, and crannies of your home at a rate much faster than it will through covered sections. The leaking process is accelerated when the winds are strong. Winds build up pressure on one side of the house, forcing cold air in, which in turn causes the inside air to flow toward the cold air by natural convection, and even faster toward the chinks on the other side through what are commonly called "drafts." Convection currents are set up in the house, which cause the air changes to multiply, again causing a further strain on the heating unit.

Research has shown that from 25 to 50 percent of heat loss is due to air infiltration. Much of this loss occurs at windows that are only single-glazed. Other losses occur through the band joists, and at chimneys, vents, outside pipes, electrical outlets, and other openings, large and small.

It is also necessary to understand the chimney effect, present in all homes, but more important in homes where there is more than one story. Basements also contribute to the chimney effect.

The chimney effect arises because of the well-known fact that heated air rises. As it does, the warm air escapes through cracks and low-R materials at the top of the home, sucking in more cold air at the bottom.

A PRETTY ACCURATE MEASURE. If you want to get a pretty good idea of how much energy you are wasting in your home, one way is to consider "fuel units." This method was adapted from federal Department of Energy guidelines and is probably the best compromise between too rough a guess and very involved mathematics.

The fuel, or heating, unit, as it is designated, is approximately 100,000 Btu. Practically speaking, it is equivalent to the useful heat from 1 gallon of oil, 120 cubic feet of natural gas, or 30 kilowatts of electricity. The cooling unit is based on the same calculations. Once you've completed all worksheets later in this chapter, you can translate the heating and cooling units back into gallons of oil (or whatever you're using) to determine the cost in wasted energy.

Remember the diagrams and checkoffs you made in Chapter 2? Soon we'll translate these into dollars and cents. But first look at the maps on the next page to determine your own heating factor. If your home has central air conditioning, add the heating and cooling zone factors to get the fuel factor for your zone, to use in the worksets on the upcoming pages. If you don't have air conditioning, use the heating factor alone.

Example. Let's take Reno, Nevada, for our example. That's located in the 1.5 heating zone. If the home is centrally air-conditioned, look at the cooling-factor map and add .5 for a combined *fuel* factor of 2.0. (Reno is actually on the dividing line, but 2.0 makes the math easier.)

(*Text continues on page 34*)

FUEL FACTORS

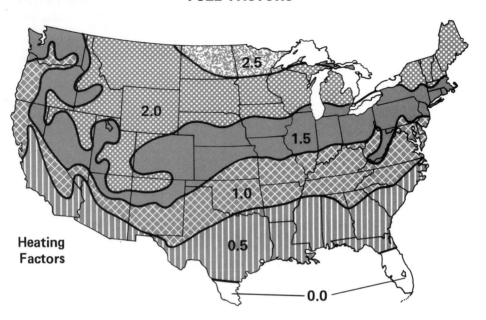

Heating Factors

Use these zone maps to find the heating and cooling factors to compute the amount of fuel loss and potential savings for your home. Instructions with sample calculations begin on page 29.

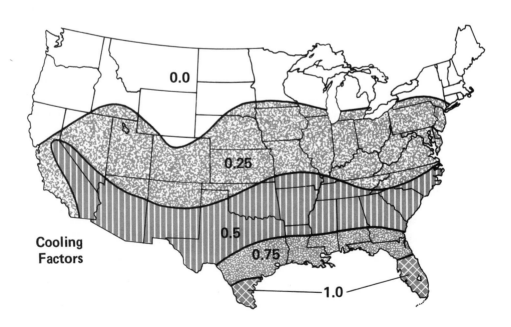

Cooling Factors

HEATING-DEGREE DAYS AND COOLING HOURS FOR MAJOR CITIES

As noted in the accompanying text, this table offers figures for computing heating and cooling needs in your region.

Winter degree days indicate the cumulative number of degrees the daily average temperatures are below 65°F. For example, a day with an average temperature of 45°F has 20 heating degree days (65 − 45 = 20). Days that average over 65°F have no heating degree days. The table shows degree days rounded to the nearest 200.

Summer cooling hours indicate the cumulative hours that temperatures are above 80°F. Figures are rounded to the nearest 50°F.

Missing numbers in the columns indicate insignificant heating and cooling needs or an absence of data.

LOCATION	WINTER DEGREE DAYS	SUMMER COOLING HOURS	LOCATION	WINTER DEGREE DAYS	SUMMER COOLING HOURS
ALABAMA			Denver	6200	650
Birmingham	2600	1350	Collins	7000	. . . .
Huntsville	3000	1250	Leadville	10600	. . . .
Mobile	1600	1850	**CONNECTICUT**		
Montgomery	2200	1600	Bridgeport	5600	300
Selma	2200	1700	Danbury	6000	350
ALASKA			Greenwich	5400	300
Anchorage	10800	. . . .	Hartford	6200	500
ARIZONA			**DELAWARE**		
Flagstaff	7200	200	Dover	4600	700
Phoenix	1800	2750	Wilmington	5000	600
Prescott	4600	1650	**DIST. OF COLUMBIA**		
Tucson	1800	2450	Washington	4200	1000
Yuma	1000	3150	**FLORIDA**		
ARKANSAS			Jacksonville	1200	1800
Fayetteville	3400	1200	Miami	200	2400
Little Rock	3200	2000	Orlando	800	1600
Texarkana	2600	1750	Pensacola	1400	1900
CALIFORNIA			**GEORGIA**		
Berkeley	3000	. . . .	Atlanta	3000	1000
Eureka	4600	. . . .	Augusta	2400	1400
Fresno	2600	1350	Brunswick	1200	1600
Long Beach	1800	250	Columbus	2400	1500
Los Angeles	2000	550	Savannah	1800	1450
Modesto	2400	1200	**HAWAII**		
Oakland	2800	100	Honolulu	. . . .	1350
Pasadena	2000	900	**IDAHO**		
Sacramento	2600	1000	Aberdeen	7000	600
San Diego	1400	150	Boise	5800	700
San Francisco	3000	. . . .	Idaho Falls	7200	350
Santa Monica	2200	150	Moscow	5800	900
Yreka	5400	. . . .	**ILLINOIS**		
COLORADO			Alton	5000	1150
Boulder	5600	. . . .	Bloomington	5600	800
Col. Springs	6400	500	Cairo	3800	1150
			Carbondale	4200	1150

(Continued)

LOCATION	WINTER DEGREE DAYS	SUMMER COOLING HOURS	LOCATION	WINTER DEGREE DAYS	SUMMER COOLING HOURS
ILLINOIS			Frederick	5000	750
Chicago	6600	750	Rockville	4400	900
Decatur	5400	950	**MASSACHUSETTS**		
De Kalb	6600	700	Boston	5600	400
Elgin	6600	700	Cape Cod	6000	150
Peoria	6000	600	Springfield	6600	400
Springfield	5400	950	Worcester	7000	300
INDIANA			**MICHIGAN**		
Bloomington	4800	850	Ann Arbor	6800	400
Columbus	5400	850	Battle Creek	6600	500
Elkhart	6400	550	Detroit	6200	500
Gary	6200	550	Escanaba	8600	250
Indianapolis	5600	750	Lansing	7000	300
IOWA			Marquette	8400	100
Cedar Falls	7400	450	Sault Ste. Marie	9400	100
Cedar Rapids	6600	550	**MINNESOTA**		
Des Moines	6600	600	Austin	8400	350
Dubuque	7400	400	Duluth	10000	....
Keokuk	5600	600	Minneapolis	8400	500
KANSAS			Moorhead	9400	400
Coffeyville	4000	1350	Rochester	8200	350
Dodge City	5000	1150	**MISSISSIPPI**		
Kansas City	4800	1100	Biloxi	1600	2050
Topeka	5200	1150	Columbus	2600	1400
Wichita	4600	1300	**MISSOURI**		
KENTUCKY			Kansas City	4800	1100
Covington	5200	750	St. Joseph	5400	1150
Lexington	4600	950	St. Louis	5000	1150
Louisville	4600	1050	**MONTANA**		
Murray	4000	1150	Billings	7000	500
LOUISIANA			Butte	9800	200
Baton Rouge	1600	1650	Great Falls	7800	300
Baton Rouge	1600	1650	Helena	8200	250
Lafayette	1400	1800	Missoula	8200	300
New Orleans	1400	1750	**NEBRASKA**		
Shreveport	2200	1850	Columbus	6600	850
MAINE			Grand Island	6600	850
Bangor	8000	200	Hastings	6200	850
Lewiston	7800	300	Lincoln	5800	1000
Portland	7600	250	Omaha	6600	900
MARYLAND			**NEVADA**		
Annapolis	4400	650	Elko	7400	650
Baltimore	4600	850	Las Vegas	2800	2350
			Reno	6400	650

LOCATION	WINTER DEGREE DAYS	SUMMER COOLING HOURS
NEW HAMPSHIRE		
Concord	7400	400
Dover	7200	300
Laconia	7800	400
Manchester	7200	500
NEW JERSEY		
Atlantic City	4800	450
Paterson	5400	600
Trenton	5000	450
NEW MEXICO		
Albuquerque	4400	1150
Carlsbad	2600	1800
Santa Fe	6200	700
NEW YORK		
Albany	6800	400
Binghamton	7200	250
Buffalo	7000	350
Hempstead	5200	450
New York	5000	650
Niagara Falls	7000	350
Poughkeepsie	6200	600
Syracuse	6800	450
White Plains	5600	400
NORTH CAROLINA		
Asheville	4000	600
Burlington	3800	900
Charlotte	3200	1150
Durham	3400	1050
Fayetteville	3000	1250
Jacksonville	2600	1250
Winston-Salem	3600	800
NORTH DAKOTA		
Bismarck	8800	450
Fargo	9200	400
Grand Forks	9800	350
Minot	9600	300
OHIO		
Akron	6000	400
Cincinnati	4400	800
Springfield	5600	800
Toledo	5800	600
Youngstown	6400	400
OKLAHOMA		
Bartlesville	4000	1350

LOCATION	WINTER DEGREE DAYS	SUMMER COOLING HOURS
Lawton	3000	1750
Moore	3200	1550
Oklahoma City	3200	1450
Ponca City	4000	1450
Tulsa	3800	1600
OREGON		
Baker	7000	200
Eugene	4800	450
Grants Pass	5000	850
Medford	5000	650
Portland	4600	200
Salem	4800	300
PENNSYLVANIA		
Allentown	5800	500
Gettysburg	5200	700
Lancaster	5400	650
Philadelphia	4400	700
Pittsburgh	6000	450
Reading	5000	800
Scranton	6200	450
RHODE ISLAND		
Newport	5800	250
Providence	6000	300
SOUTH CAROLINA		
Charleston	2000	1250
Columbia	2400	1350
Myrtle Beach	....	1200
Spartanburg	3000	1100
Walhalla	3200	1100
SOUTH DAKOTA		
Aberdeen	8600	550
Huron	8200	650
Rapid City	7400	550
Sioux Falls	7800	500
TENNESSEE		
Chattanooga	3200	1250
Johnson City	4000	850
Knoxville	3400	1000
Memphis	3200	1500
Nashville	3600	1300
TEXAS		
Abilene	2600	2000
Amarillo	4000	1200

(Continued)

(Heating-Degree-Days table continued)

LOCATION	WINTER DEGREE DAYS	SUMMER COOLING HOURS	LOCATION	WINTER DEGREE DAYS	SUMMER COOLING HOURS
TEXAS			Richmond	3800	1000
Austin	1800	2250	Roanoke	4200	800
Brownsville	600	2300	**WASHINGTON**		
Corpus Christi	1000	2550	Bellingham	5400	150
Dallas	2400	2300	Olympia	5200	100
El Paso	2800	1850	Seattle	5200	100
Galveston	1200	2650	Spokane	6600	350
Killeen	2000	2000	Tacoma	5200	100
Longview	2400	1850	Walla Walla	4800	600
Lubbock	3600	1350	**WEST VIRGINIA**		
San Antonio	1600	2000	Charleston	4400	800
Victoria	1200	2300	Huntington	4400	1000
			Wheeling	5200	450
UTAH			**WISCONSIN**		
Ogden	5600	800	Beloit	6800	600
Salt Lake City	6000	900	Green Bay	8000	250
VERMONT			La Crosse	7600	500
Burlington	8200	300	Madison	7800	500
Montpelier	8800	300	Racine	7400	350
Rutland	8000	300	Superior	9800	200
VIRGINIA			**WYOMING**		
Alexandria	4200	1000	Casper	7400	550
Norfolk	3400	1000	Lander	7800	200
Petersburg	3600	1000	Sheridan	7600	600

(Text continued from page 29)

If you want to be even more precise in your calculations, you can use the *actual* heating factor in your particular locale by determining the number of winter degree-days in your city or town and dividing by 4000. The Department of Energy has already done this on the topmost map on page 30, by using 1.0 for 4000 degree days, 1.5 for 6000 degree-days, etc. For central A/C, divide summer degree-days by 2000 and add to the heating factor. The table "Heating-Degree Days and Cooling Hours for Major Cities" (page 31) tells you the actual heating/cooling figures for cities in the U.S. If you live elsewhere, you can find your annual degree-days from the local utility, oil supplier, or weather station. Or use the nearest city on the table. Reno, for example, has 6400 winter degree-days. Dividing by 4000 gives us a heating factor of 1.6. The summer degree-days are 650, divided by 2000, for a .4 cooling factor. That's a 1.9 fuel factor—pretty close to our 2.0, resulting when we combine the map factors on page 30.

Be warned, though, that the calculations get a little messy doing it this way. The zone fuel factors used in this book are close enough to yield a quite accurate picture of thermal loss for most places within each heating zone. (Exceptions might be homes that are in high mountain areas.)

Now take out the diagrams and notes you prepared in Chapter 2. You'll need

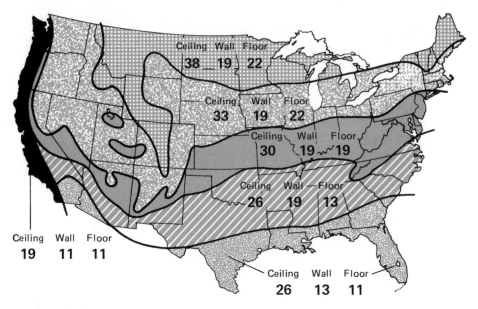

Ceiling Wall Floor
38 — 19 ⟩ 22

Ceiling Wall Floor
33   19 ⟩ 22

Ceiling Wall Floor
30 ⟨ 19 ⤳ 19

Ceiling Wall — Floor
⤳ 26   19 / 13 \

Ceiling Wall Floor
19   11   11

Ceiling Wall Floor
26   13   11

This map, adapted from an Owens-Corning original, indicates insulation recommendations for various parts of the U.S. Note that the insulating zones combine both heating and cooling requirements.

them to make computations in the worksheets that follow. The worksheets will
help you determine how much fuel you're wasting now, what your future fuel
costs can be, and the potential savings from performing some of the projects
described in this book.

Ceiling computations. The first worksheet in the series, beginning on page 41, is
titled "CEILINGS: Conduction Losses & Savings." It can be used by itself to compute your present ceiling losses and those you could expect after insulating and
other weatherizing. Or the results from the ceiling worksheet can be combined
with those on succeeding worksheets on walls, floors, infiltration, and single-
glass windows—all entered in the final worksheet in the series titled "BALANCE
SHEET." By completing some or all worksheets you'll have a good idea where
you stand and where you might best begin upgrading things. Let's look at the
ceilings worksheet, as an example.

Step 1 asks you to enter names, thicknesses, and R-values of all materials, beginning from the inside surface out. (Note: For R-values consult the table "R-
Values of House Components," on page 40.)

Step 2 first asks that you enter the square footage for the *top floor* of your
home, as you computed it in Chapter 2. Remember, if the ceiling isn't a single
rectangle or square, divide it into rectangles, computing each separately. Next
enter the fuel factor for your zone, either from the foregoing maps or from
your own calculations of heating-degree days and cooling hours. (If you have
central A/C, use a combined heating and cooling fuel factor.) Divide the product of ceiling area multiplied times the fuel factor by the total R-value you

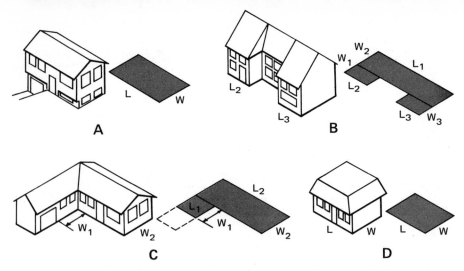

A

B

C

D

To figure the ceiling area of your house, multiply length times width for the simple perimeter as shown in drawing A. The house in B is divided into squares, which are computed separately and added. C and D show a couple of pitfalls: For C, deduct the area above an unheated garage. With D's partially sloping roof, use the larger area just above the ceiling, unless the top story is heated, in which case you should use the smaller area on top of the roof.

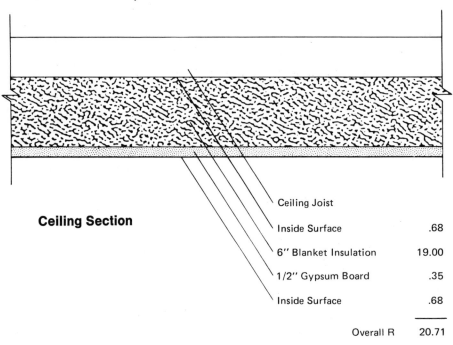

Ceiling Section

Ceiling Joist

Inside Surface	.68
6" Blanket Insulation	19.00
1/2" Gypsum Board	.35
Inside Surface	.68
Overall R	20.71

tallied in Step 1. The result is the present fuel units you can expect to lose in an average year.

Step 3 is computed much like Step 2 except that you divide by recommended R-values for ceilings in your zone. The result is future fuel units (FFU), the amount of fuel units you could expect to be losing with optimum insulation.

Step 4 simply asks you to subtract future fuel-unit losses from present fuel-unit losses to determine potential fuel-unit savings. Then enter all three figures in the shaded totals onto the final worksheet, titled "BALANCE SHEET."

Wall and floor computations. The procedures for the wall and floor computations are the same as for the ceilings. Subtract the total window and door area from total wall area. When you determine the three shaded numbers for each (PFU, FFU, and PFS), enter them on the "BALANCE SHEET."

Air-infiltration computations. Computing fuel loss from air infiltration is similar to that for ceilings, walls, and floors, except that here there are no exact figures to go by. Study the notes and checkmarks made in Chapter 2. Then make a judgment according to the three categories on the worksheet titled "IN-FILTRATION: Heat Losses and Savings." Next, simply follow the steps.

The result of all these calculations tells you how much fuel is being lost by air infiltration. You will never get that figure down to zero, but you should be able to get each category down to one air change per hour with proper weather-stripping, caulking, and similar measures. To determine the future fuel units after installing these weatherizing devices, perform the same calculations as above, but this time make the draft index 1.0. Subtract the future fuel-unit (FFU) loss from the present fuel-unit (PFU) loss to get the potential fuel savings (PFS).

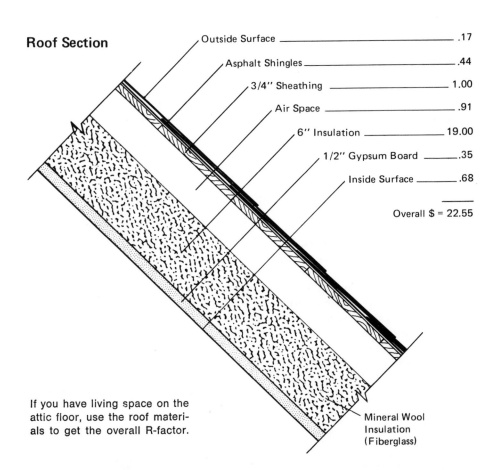

Roof Section

Outside Surface —————————— .17

Asphalt Shingles —————————— .44

3/4" Sheathing ———————— 1.00

Air Space ———————— .91

6" Insulation —————— 19.00

1/2" Gypsum Board ———.35

Inside Surface ———— .68

Overall $ = 22.55

If you have living space on the attic floor, use the roof materials to get the overall R-factor.

Mineral Wool Insulation (Fiberglass)

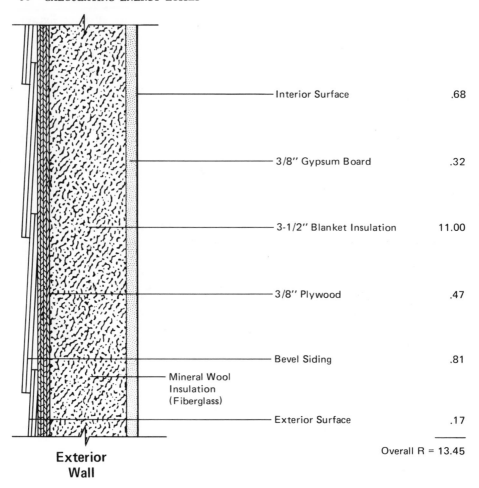

Interior Surface	.68
3/8" Gypsum Board	.32
3-1/2" Blanket Insulation	11.00
3/8" Plywood	.47
Bevel Siding	.81
Exterior Surface	.17

Mineral Wool
Insulation
(Fiberglass)

Overall R = 13.45

**Exterior
Wall**

This is how the R-values of the materials in a typical wall are added to compute the overall R-factor.

Heat loss through windows. To determine the amount of heat loss through windows, compute the total window area and multiply by the heating factor for your zone. For single-pane windows with no storm sash, the figure equals the present fuel units required. (The R-value of a single-pane window is 1.0.) Double-glazed windows or storm windows are excluded because not much can be done to make them more weathertight. We've already included savings by weatherstripping and caulking in our air-infiltration figures, so the only future fuel savings on windows is accomplished by adding storm sash. To get the potential savings, divide the present fuel units on the single-glass windows by 2. Enter this on the "BALANCE SHEET."

Getting the totals. At this point, all the blanks on the "BALANCE SHEET" should be filled. Now add up all the figures. The first column is the total number of fuel units presently being consumed. The second column is the estimated fu-

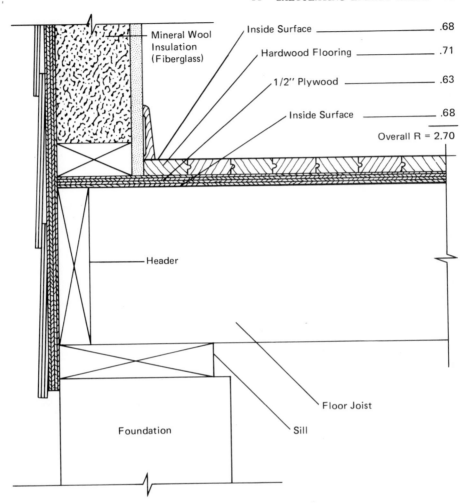

Inside Surface	.68
Hardwood Flooring	.71
1/2" Plywood	.63
Inside Surface	.68
	Overall R = 2.70

Mineral Wool Insulation (Fiberglass)

Header

Floor Joist

Foundation

Sill

This is typical floor construction.

ture fuel units after all the weatherizing steps have been completed. The third column is the total potential savings (subtract column 2 from column 1).

What we now have is the estimated heating and/or cooling units which can be saved by weatherizing your home as completely as possible. This is not to say you will—or should—do so, or that it is even feasible to do that thorough a job. That topic is discussed in the next chapter. But these computations will give you a pretty good idea how much thermal loss occurs in your home each year and what the theoretical savings can be.

To put the final calculations in more practical terms, meaning how many gallons of oil, therms of natural gas, or kilowatts of electricity are being wasted each year, multiply the fuel-unit figure by 1 (oil), 120 (natural gas), or 30 (kilowatt-hours). In our example, we found that potential fuel savings (PFS) were 1037 units yearly.

In terms of gallons of oil, that's exactly 1037 gallons (1 heating unit equals 1 gallon of oil). In terms of natural gas, it's 124,440 cubic feet (multiply by 120). For electricity users, it's 31,110 kilowatt-hours of electricity that are being wasted (multiply by 30).

The final calculations translate the potential savings into dollars. You need the local costs per unit to do this. If you don't already know them, look at your last utility or oil bill to find the rate, or call your oil or utility dealer. Better, determine what the costs will be next year, if possible. In my area, for example, I know that oil prices may soon average 60 cents a gallon. If our sample house were my own (it isn't), I'd multiply the last figure for oil by 60 to get $622.20. Terrific. But is it realistic? You'll find out in the next chapter.

R-VALUES OF HOUSE COMPONENTS

MATERIAL	THICKNESS	R-VALUE
AIR FILM AND SPACES		
Air space, bounded by ordinary materials	¾″ or more	0.91
Air space, bounded by aluminum foil	¾″ or more	2.17
Exterior surface resistance	—	0.17
Interior surface resistance	—	0.68
MASONRY		
Sand and gravel concrete block	8″	1.11
Sand and gravel concrete block	12″	1.28
Lightweight concrete block	8″	2.00
Lightweight concrete block	12″	2.13
Face brick	4″	0.44
Concrete cast in place	8″	0.64
BUILDING MATERIALS (GENERAL)		
Wood sheathing or subfloor	¾″	1.00
Fiber board insulating sheathing	¾″	2.10
Plywood	⅝″	0.79
Plywood	½″	0.63
Plywood	⅜″	0.47
Bevel lapped siding	½″ x 8″	0.81
Bevel lapped siding	¾″ x 10″	1.05
Vertical tongue and groove board	¾″	1.00
Drop siding	¾″	0.94
Asbestos board	¼″	0.13
⅜″ gypsum lath and ⅜″ plaster	¾″	0.42
Gypsum board	⅜″	0.32
Interior plywood panel	¼″	0.31
Building paper	—	0.06
Vapor barrier	—	'0.00
Wood shingles	—	0.87
Asphalt shingles	—	0.44
Linoleum	—	0.08
Carpet with fiber pad	—	2.08
Hardwood floor	—	0.71
INSULATION MATERIALS (MINERAL WOOL, GLASS WOOL, WOOD WOOL, ETC.)		
Blanket or batts	1″	3.70
Blanket or batts	3½″	11.00
Blanket or batts	6″	19.00
Loose fill	1″	3.33
Rigid insulation board (sheathing)	¾″	2.10
WINDOWS AND DOORS		
Single window	—	Approx. 1.00
Double window	—	Approx. 2.00
Exterior door	—	Approx. 2.00

CEILINGS: Conduction Losses & Savings
(See completed sample for guidance.)

Step 1.

Material	Thickness (inches)		R Value
Inside surface	—		0.68
Inside surface (0.68) or Outside surface (0.17)	—		
		Total R-value	

Step 2.

☐ × ☐ ÷ ☐ = ☐

Ceiling area (sq. ft.) × Fuel factor (your zone) ÷ Total R-value (from Step 1 rounded to nearest tenths) = Present fuel units (PFU) loss

Step 3.

☐ × ☐ ÷ ☐ = ☐

Ceiling area (sq. ft.) × Fuel factor (your zone) ÷ Recommended R-value for ceilings = Future fuel units (FFU) loss

Step 4. Subtract future fuel-unit loss from present fuel unit loss to determine potential fuel savings.

☐ Potential fuel savings (PFS)

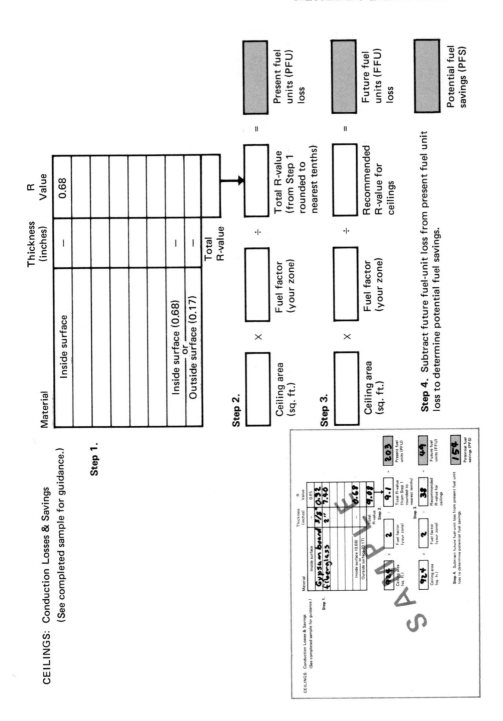

WALLS: Conduction Losses & Savings (See completed sample for guidance.)

Step 1.

Material	Thickness (Inches)	R Value
Interior surface	–	0.68
Outside surface	–	.17
Total R-value		

$\div$

Total R-Value from Step 1, rounded to nearest tenths	Fuel factor (your zone)	= Present fuel-unit (PFU) loss

$\div$

Recommended R-Value for walls	Fuel factor (your zone)	= Future fuel-unit (FFU) loss

Step 2.

	×	
Total perimeter of outside wall (ft.)		Total height of outside wall (ft.)

=

Gross wall area (sq. ft.)

Step 3.

	–	
Gross wall area (sq. ft.)		Total area of windows, doors (sq. ft.)

=

Net wall area (sq. ft.)

Step 4.

Net wall area (sq. ft.) × Fuel factor (your zone)

Step 5.

Net wall area (sq. ft.) × Fuel factor (your zone)

Step 6. Subtract future fuel units from present fuel units to determine potential fuel savings.

Potential fuel-savings (PFS)

WALLS: Conduction Losses & Savings (See completed sample for guidance.)

Step 1.

Material	Thickness (Inches)	R Value
Interior surface	–	0.68
Gypsum Bd. 3/8	3/8	0.32
Air Space	2"	0.41
Fiberglass	2"	7.40
Sheathing		1.00
Asbestos		
Shingles		.13
Outside surface	–	.17
Total R-value		10.11

10.6 ÷ 2 = **154** Present fuel-unit (PFU) loss

2.2 ÷ 2 = **74** Future fuel-unit (FFU) loss

Step 2. 122 × 8 = 976

Step 3. 976 – 158 = 818

Step 4. 818

Step 5. 818

Step 6. Subtract future fuel units from present fuel units to determine potential fuel savings. **80** Potential fuel-savings (PFS)

SAMPLE

FLOORS: Conduction Losses & Savings

Step 1. To compute R-value of your present floor, list all materials including carpet but excluding floor joists.

Interior Surface	– – –	.68
Interior Surface	– – –	.68

Step 2.

$$\text{Floor area (sq. ft.)} \times \frac{\text{Fuel factor (your zone)}}{\text{Total R-value}} = \text{Present fuel-unit (PFU) loss}$$

Step 3.

$$\text{Floor area} \times \frac{\text{Fuel factor (your zone)}}{\text{Recommended R-value for floors}} = \text{Future fuel-unit (FFU) loss}$$

Step 4. Subtract future fuel-unit loss from present fuel-unit loss to determine potential fuel savings.

Potential fuel savings (PFS)

SAMPLE

FLOORS: Conduction Losses & Savings

Step 1. To compute R-value of your present floor, list all materials including carpet but excluding floor joists.

Interior Surface	– – –	.68
Linoleum		.08
Plywood	½"	.65
Subfloor	⅝	1.00
Interior Surface	– – –	.68

Step 2.

$$924 \times \frac{2}{3.1} = 596 \text{ (Present fuel-unit (PFU) loss)}$$

Total R-value

Step 3.

$$924 \times \frac{2}{19} = 97 \text{ (Future fuel-unit (FFU) loss)}$$

Recommended R-value for floors

Step 4. Subtract future fuel-unit loss from present fuel-unit loss to determine potential fuel savings.

499 Potential fuel savings (PFS)

INFILTRATION: Heat Losses & Savings

Step 1. House Draft Index: Opposite each of the four component parts of a building in the table below, place a check mark in the circle adjacent to the features which best describe the condition of the building.

Building Component	One air change per hour (1)	Two air changes per hour (2)	Three air changes per hour (3)
Cellar or Crawl Space	Tight, no cracks, caulked sills, sealed cellar windows, no grade entrance leaks ◯ Plywood floor, no trap door leaks, no leaks around water, sewer, and electrical openings	Some foundation cracks, loose cellar windows, grade entrance not tight ◯ Tongue-and-groove board floor, reasonable fit on trap doors, around pipes	Major foundation cracks, poor seal around grade entrance ◯ Board floor, loose fit around pipes
Windows	Storm windows with good fit ◯	No storm windows, good fit on regular windows ◯	No storm windows, loose fit on regular windows ◯
Doors	Good fit on storm doors ◯	Loose storm doors, poor fit on inside door ◯	No storm doors, loose fit on inside door ◯
Walls	Caulked windows and doors, building paper used under siding ◯	Caulking in poor repair, building needs paint ◯	No indication of building paper, evident cracks around door and window frame ◯

Step 2. Multiply the number of check marks in the first column by 1, the second column by 2, and the third column by 3. The Draft Index will be the sum of these products, divided by 4.

Step 3.

[Floor area (sq. ft.)] X [Height to ceiling (to upstairs ceiling in two-story house) (ft.)] = [Volume of air in building (cu. ft.)]

Step 4.

[Volume of air in building] X [Draft index (from Step 2)] X [Fuel factor (your zone)] X .02 = [Present fuel-unit (PFU) loss]

Step 5. Potential Savings by Reducing Infiltration: It should be possible to reduce the draft index for a building to 1 (that is, reduce the number of air changes to one per hour). If the draft index for this building were improved to 1, the infiltration loss would be:

[Volume (from above)] X [**1** Draft index] X [Fuel factor (your zone)] X .02 = [Future fuel-unit (FFU) loss]

Step 6. Subtract future fuel-unit loss from present fuel-unit loss to determine potential fuel savings.

[Potential fuel savings (PFS)]

SINGLE-GLASS & DOUBLE-GLASS EFFECTS

Step 1. Area of Single Glass Windows   (Assuming single-glass has an R-value of 1): Note, if you have only double-glass windows, disregard this worksheet and go to the "Balance Sheet," next.

Width	×	Height	×	Number	=	Area

Total sq. ft.

Step 2.

Total sq. ft. × Fuel factor (your zone) = Present fuel-unit (PFU) loss

Step 3. Double glazing or adding storm windows will cut the heat loss by half. So divide heating units directly by two as shown.

Present fuel-unit (PFU) loss ÷ 2 = Potential fuel savings PFS

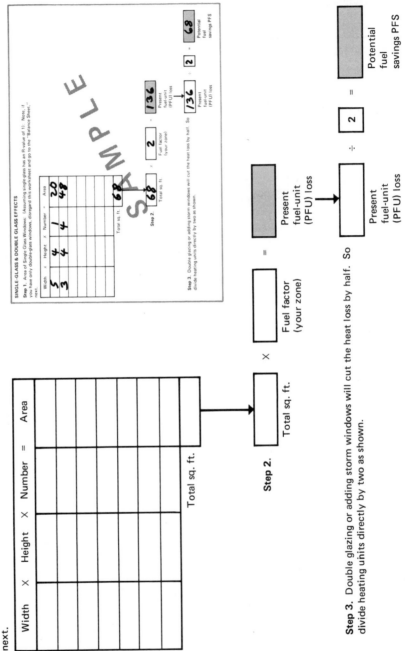

BALANCE SHEET: Overall Heat Losses and Potential Savings. Here enter the figures on present fuel units (PFU), future fuel units (FFU), and potential fuel savings (PFS) from the worksheets you completed on previous pages.

Type of Heat Loss	PFU	FFU	PFS
Ceilings			
Walls			
Floors			
Infiltration			
Single-Glass			
TOTALS			

BALANCE SHEET: Overall Heat Losses and Potential Savings Here enter the figures on present fuel units (PFU), future fuel units (FFU), and potential fuel savings (PFS) from the worksheets you completed on previous pages.

Type of Heat Loss	PFU	FFU	PFS
Ceilings	203	49	154
Walls	154	74	80
Floors	576	97	499
Infiltration	532	296	236
Single-Glass	136	68	68
TOTALS	1621	584	1037

5 | Is the Job Worth Doing?

IF YOU ASKED which of the jobs in this book was worth doing way back in the good old days before 1973, the answer would be few or none. When energy costs were low, it hardly paid to retrofit your home with insulation, weather-stripping, or caulking. If you were paying less than 20 cents for a gallon of oil and had your walls sprayed with plastic foam, it would take decades to get your investment back. You might weatherstrip a drafty door, but only to stop the cold air from whistling in, not to save fuel.

Those decades that it would have taken you to recoup your insulation invest-ment are called the "payback" period. Payback means the length of time it takes for the savings in fuel to equal the money spent in weatherization. To take an oversimplified example:

Assume it will take 24 rolls of insulation at $10 a roll to bring your attic up to the recommended level. The cost is $240. This will save 100 gallons of oil a year. If the oil costs 60 cents a gallon, that means you'll save $60 a year. In four years, your $240 investment will be repaid. Every year after that is a $60 dividend. And it'll probably be more, because the price of fuel is certainly headed up, not down. If the price of fuel increases shortly after you complete your installation, the payback period is also shortened.

The actual computations for your home will be a little more complicated, but not much more so. The principle is the same, and the tables and worksheets in this chapter will help.

Let's take another example. Assume your walls already have some insulation. Assume the time is way back in 1973. You live in a relatively warm climate without central air conditioning. To have someone blow cellulose into your walls costs $1000. The estimated fuel saving is 50 heating units of natural gas per year at 20 cents per unit (120 cubic feet). You'll save $10 a year. The payback period is 100 years—obviously, a lousy investment. Now the time is the present. You're paying four times as much for gas, and you reconsider. Now the pay-back period is 25 years—and it's still a lousy investment. Besides, the cost of having the work done has probably increased too.

The last example is an extreme one, but is used to illustrate the fact that it isn't *always* wise to jump in and perform all the weatherization tasks in this book. The more the job costs, the longer the payback and the more you should investigate the economics of it.

The payback period is your most important figure. There are other considerations, though, such as alternate uses for the money. If you put $1000 into a savings account, it will double in 12 years or so, depending on the interest rate, which is equivalent to a 12-year payback period. You have to do better than that with your weatherization project, if economics is the only consideration.

If you have to borrow money to insulate your home, the cost of the borrowed money must also be considered, in effect lengthening the payback period. You should also estimate what effect your project will have on the resale value of your home, and how long you expect to live there. Future fuel prices should be considered, as well. The almost certain rise in price also has the effect of shortening the payback time, and tax credits are important. Noneconomic factors should be considered, too, as we've discussed before—a well-insulated home would be more comfortable, and you would be conserving energy.

Such variables as prevailing interest rates, future fuel costs, resale value, and personal comfort cannot be measured here. You certainly should take them into account, but the overriding factor in any weatherization project is the payback period. After that is established, then the other matters can and should be estimated individually.

In most cases, the value of the specific project will be immediately obvious from the payback period alone. Attic insulation, for example, when it is done by the homeowner, will probably have a short payback period. If the payback is less than seven years, there is no better investment anywhere. Those that take up to ten years to repay are probably good, too. Any project which takes more than ten years to repay will be questionable. Then such things as interest rates, expected fuel increases, and comfort will have to come into play when you make your decision.

We can make one generalization here. Do-it-yourself projects will almost always be worthwhile. Contracted jobs will usually be questionable. Because it's questionable, however, doesn't mean that it shouldn't be done. You just have to work a little harder to figure out its value to you.

To determine what each of the jobs in the preceding chapter will cost, check local supply sources (including availability) and make the calculations on the "Cost Estimates" worksheet at the end of this chapter. Enter these figures and the others from Chapter 4 on the "Bottom Line" table. The left side of the table gives potential dollar savings, computed as discussed in Chapter 4.

On the right side of the "Bottom Line" table, the weatherization cost ("Cost to Improve") is adjusted to allow for any tax credit (see below) or loan charges and interest to get the true cost. Divide the actual cost by the potential dollar savings to get the payback period. After you have the payback period for each job, you should have a good idea as to whether it's worthwhile. For any questionable payback period, also consider the other factors discussed above. If you come up with a payback of ten years, for example, check with the local utility or fuel dealer and ask him what the expected future costs might be in those ten years. They should have a good idea, since rate increases must be submitted to government agencies in advance.

If your fuel costs are expected to double over the next ten years, that will shorten the true payback period considerably. You won't be able to factor this exactly, but it should help make up your mind.

Watch the news, too. What's happening in the volatile Middle East these days? Is another war a good possibility? If so, expect higher fuel costs. Have any new big oil fields been discovered? Have there been any dramatic break-throughs in new forms of energy? If anything like this has happened, future fuel costs may not be so bad. As of this writing, however, there is little to be optimistic about.

The one big question left hanging is the tax credit for insulation and other weatherization projects. Check with your local and state officials on this.

Our example uses a 25 percent credit, which is a hypothetical one. On your worksheet, use whatever percentage is in effect. A column is also provided for adding the charges and interest on any loan you may have to take out. Our example assumes no loan costs, but add them if they apply. As you can see, both of those columns will make a significant difference in the true cost and payback period.

SOME COMMENTS ON THE SAMPLE TABLES. Along with the worksheets that are for your use, I have given sample tables for a hypothetical house. It is important to realize that the example is exactly that—an example. Do not draw from it false conclusions concerning your own house, such as assuming that the payback period for floor insulation is always shorter than that for ceilings or walls. For one thing, your floors may not be amenable to full insulation. If your house is built on a slab, there are ways to cut down on thermal loss (see Chapter 9), but it will be impossible to bring the R-value to R-19.

Furthermore, it has been assumed in the example that there is already some insulation in the ceiling and walls and none in the basement. You can always save more by starting your weatherization in areas where the total R is the lowest. In my example, floor insulation should have first priority, but not necessarily in your home.

It is also assumed in the example that an insulation contractor will charge more, proportionately, to blow insulation into a small home than a large one. There are certain fixed costs, such as bringing the men and equipment to the site, which usually raise the cost per square foot of wall area on a small home. The relative R-value will be cheaper for a larger home. Also note that the total R-value of the wall may exceed the local recommendations. This is because there is no point in having a contractor blow in just a specified amount of insulation. He should fill the wall completely. It won't cost any more. And it is also assumed that the cost per R-value of the blown-in insulation will be roughly the same, regardless of the type. The $600 figure given in our example represents a rough minimum cost for such a home.

Finally, it should be understood that the prices given in the sample table are for one region at the time of this writing. Costs may fluctuate widely in other areas at any given time.

All that being said, however, a few generalizations can be drawn from our example. First, it is wisest to insulate an area which doesn't have any already. Although there is some truth to the often-heard maxim that the ceiling is the most important place to insulate, it is also true that thermal loss occurs throughout the entire house. If there is no insulation in the floors and some in the attic, it is probably more cost-efficient to start with the floors.

It should also be evident from the example that caulking and weatherstripping are among the best ways to cut down on thermal loss. Plastic storms are also a good investment even though they will probably last for only one season.

COST ESTIMATES

ATTIC INSULATION

1. Attic area (sq. ft.) ___
2. Recommended level ___
3. Existing level ___
4. Add ___
5. Cost/sq. ft. ___
6. Total cost (1 × 5) ___

WALL INSULATION (BLOWN-IN)

1. Wall area (sq. ft.) ___
2. Recommended level ___
3. Existing level ___
4. Add ___
5. Cost/sq. ft. ___
6. Total cost (1 × 5) ___

FLOOR INSULATION

1. Floor area (sq. ft.) ___
2. Recommended level ___
3. Existing level ___
4. Add ___
5. Cost/sq. ft. ___
6. Total cost (1 × 5) ___

WEATHERSTRIPPING (MATERIALS ONLY)

1. Linear feet ___
2. Cost per foot ___
3. Total cost ___

CAULKING (MATERIALS ONLY)

1. Variable costs ___
2. Estimated cost ___

STORM WINDOWS

size (sq. ft.)	number	cost each	sub-total
___	___	___	___
___	___	___	___
___	___	___	___

Total cost ___

COST ESTIMATES (SAMPLE)

ATTIC INSULATION

1. Attic area (sq. ft.) — 924
2. Recommended level — R-38
3. Existing level — R-7
4. Add — R-30
5. Cost/sq. ft. — .30
6. Total cost (1 × 5) — 275 DO IT YOURSELF / $25 CONTRACTOR

WALL INSULATION (BLOWN-IN)

1. Wall area (sq. ft.) — 818
2. Recommended level — R-22*
3. Existing level — R-11
4. Add — .75*
5. Cost/sq. ft. — 600
6. Total cost (1 × 5)

FLOOR INSULATION

1. Floor area (sq. ft.) — 924
2. Recommended level — R-19
3. Existing level — R-3
4. Add — R-16
5. Cost/sq. ft. — .20
6. Total cost (1 × 5) — 185

WEATHERSTRIPPING (MATERIALS ONLY)

1. Linear feet — 300
2. Cost per foot — .10
3. Total cost — 30

CAULKING (MATERIALS ONLY)

1. Variable costs — 40-80
2. Estimated cost — 60

$90 {

STORM WINDOWS

size (sq. ft.)	number	cost each	sub-total
20	1	33	33
12	4	28	112

Total cost — 150 — Triple Track / 10 — PLASTIC

*Minimum for small house. See text for comments.

THE BOTTOM LINE (SAMPLE)

IMPROVEMENT	POTENTIAL FUEL SAVINGS $	FUEL COST (EXPECTED)	POTENTIAL $ SAVINGS	$ COST TO IMPROVE	LOAN COST	$ TAX CREDIT	ACTUAL $ COST	POTENTIAL $ SAVINGS	PAYBACK (YEARS)
Insulate Ceiling				(add R-30)					
a) Plastic Sheets	154 ×	60¢ =	92.40	275.00 +	0 −	68.75 =	206.25 ÷	92.40 =	2.2
b) Contractor				400.00 +	0 −	100.00 =	300.00 ÷	92.40 =	3.2
Blown-in Wall Insulation	74 ×	60¢ =	44.40	600.00 +	0 −	150.00 =	450.00 ÷	44.40 =	10.1
Insulate Floors	499 ×	60¢ =	299.40	(add R-19) 185.00 +	0 −	46.25 =	138.75 ÷	299.40 =	0.5
Reduce Air Infiltration	236 ×	60¢ =	141.60	90.00 +	0 −	22.50 =	67.50 ÷	141.60 =	0.5
Double-Glaze All Windows									
a) Plastic Sheets	68 ×	60¢ =	40.80	10.00 +	0 −	22.50 =	7.50 ÷	40.80 =	0.2
b) Alum. Storms				150.00 +	0 −	37.50 =	112.50 ÷	40.80 =	2.8
Total or Median	1031 ×	60¢ =	618.60	1160.00 to 1425.00 +	0 −	290.00 to 356.25 =	870.00 to 1068.75 ÷	618.60 =	1.4 to 1.7

THE BOTTOM LINE (FOR YOUR CALCULATIONS)

IMPROVEMENT	POTENTIAL FUEL SAVINGS $	FUEL COST (EXPECTED)	POTENTIAL $ SAVINGS	$ COST TO IMPROVE	LOAN COST	$ TAX CREDIT	ACTUAL $ COST	POTENTIAL $ SAVINGS	PAYBACK (YEARS)
Insulate Ceiling									
a) D-I-Y	×	=		++	−	=	÷	=	
b) Contractor					−	=	÷	=	
Blown-in Wall Insulation	×	=		+	−	=	÷	=	
Insulate Floors	×	=		+	−	=	÷	=	
Reduce Air Infiltration	×	=		+	−	=	÷	=	
Double-Glaze All Windows									
a) Plastic Sheets	×	=		++	−	=	÷	=	
b) Alum. Storms					−	=	÷	=	
Total or Median									

6 | Insulating Materials

CHAPTERS LIKE THIS usually begin something like "There is a wide variety of materials available to the homeowner . . . " It isn't true, though. The fact is that there are only a few realistic choices, and it isn't at all difficult to find out which is best for your particular job. Furthermore, as of this writing and into the foreseeable future, you may have a great deal of difficulty getting *any* kind of insulating material. Whatever you can find, you'll use.

People have gotten smarter over the past couple of years. Realization has set in that you can indeed reduce your fuel costs, increase your comfort, and help with the energy shortage by intelligent use of insulation. The insulation manufacturers have been expanding production greatly, but it'll be a few years yet before they catch up to the surge in demand.

I took an extensive tour of likely insulation dealers in the New York metropolitan area and found that only about 20 percent of the dealers had any insulating materials at all. Some had a minimal supply. Others promised that they'd have some "in a few days." Most just said to forget it. None had a wide choice of types or sizes. The big chain, Rickel's, seemed to be the only dealer with close to an adequate supply or any variety. I visited several Rickel's stores during the winter of '77–'78 and they had R-11 and R-19 fiberglass blankets, all with foil facing. They also had some loose cellulose pour. A few stores had some plastic foam if you got there early. And that was it. Furthermore, no customer could buy more than 25 rolls.

The truth of the matter is that for do-it-yourselfers, the choice will be limited for the rest of the 1970s and perhaps beyond. There are a few options, but you'll probably take what you can get and manage somehow.

INSULATION DEFINED. Contrary to general belief, the value of an insulating material does not lie in the material itself. Neither fiberglass, nor cellulose, nor plastic foam stops the flow of heat energy. Take fiberglass, for example. It's made of glass, a very poor insulator.

Fiberglass *insulation* is another story—not because it is any different in chemical makeup, but because of the way it is split into tiny fibers which trap air. The *air* is really the insulator.

Why, then, don't we just use air itself as an insulator? We do, in some cases, such as in storm and double-glazed windows. But air by itself is not a good insulator, either, because when heated it allows agitation of the air molecules,

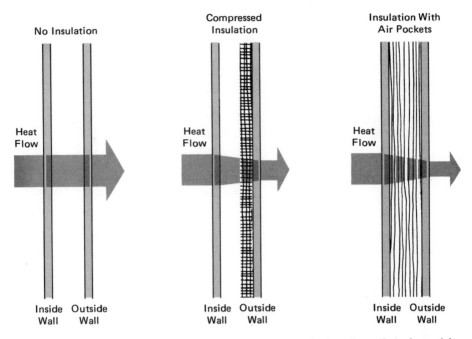

No Insulation

Compressed
Insulation

Insulation With
Air Pockets

Heat
Flow

Heat
Flow

Heat
Flow

Inside   Outside
Wall   Wall

Inside   Outside
Wall   Wall

Inside   Outside
Wall   Wall

It's not the insulation materials themselves that count; it's the air pockets formed by their construction. When insulation is compressed, as in the middle drawing, heat flow is almost as great as when there is no insulation at all.

which in turn transfer the heat from the warm side by convection, or movement of heat energy.

The trick is to "stratify" air, or trap it into minute particles so that little movement is allowed. If the air cannot move, it cannot transfer heat energy as quickly. (Remember, we can never completely stop the flow of heat. All we can do is slow it down.)

Theoretically, the best insulator is a vacuum, with no air molecules to transmit the heat. This is the principle of the thermos bottle. If we could design a house like a thermos bottle, we wouldn't need insulation. Obviously, we can't, unless we want a house we can't leave or enter.

The next best thing is to find a medium that has the least amount of molecules, so that there is less heat transmission. Anyone who has studied any chemistry knows that the elements with the least amount of molecules by volume are gases such as hydrogen and helium. For various reasons, such as cost, explosiveness, and toxicity, we can't use most of these cases.

Air, however, is a gas. It's plentiful and cheap, so we use that. But because of the mobility of air molecules, we must partition it into enclosures that are as small as possible. The partitioning material, too, should be thin and light, but in and of itself the material does not insulate. If we squeeze or compress any insulating material until all the air pockets are gone, it becomes a solid mass, which is virtually worthless as insulation.

R Factors and Insulation Thickness

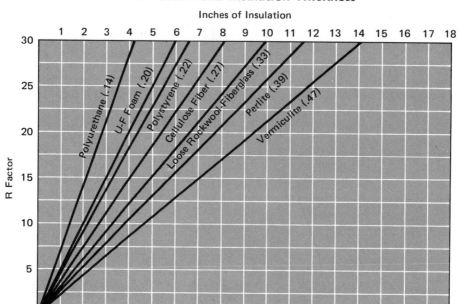

This graph demonstrates that the K-value (shown above in parentheses) of any material is inversely proportional to its R-value. In practical terms, it will take, for example, 14 inches of vermiculite (K-47) to provide the same amount of thermal resistance (R) as 6 inches of ureaformaldehyde foam (K-20).

The graph above shows graphically how the common types of home insulation compare in terms of K-values and R-values (see Chapter 4). Polyurethane, though not readily available for home use, with a K-factor of .14, gives the best R-value. Vermiculite, with a K-factor of .47, has the poorest R-value. To reach R-30, you need only 6 inches of foam, but 14 inches of vermiculite. But there is more to be considered than pure K and R designations.

One of these factors is cost. Others are availability, safety, and ease of installation. Affecting all of these considerations is an important question: Can you do it yourself? If you can install your own insulation, you will save money, and in most cases get a higher R-value per dollar expended.

No one insulating material insulates any *better* than any other type. The most important consideration is the R-value, but there are other factors, too. The table on the next page shows some of these factors.

Regardless of the other considerations, however, mineral-wool blankets rated at R-30 will insulate exactly the same as poured cellulose rated at R-3.0 per inch laid 10 inches thick (3.0 × 10 = 30). Some products, such as ureaformaldehyde foam, will give more insulating effect per inch, and may therefore be a better choice where space is narrow (such as in closed walls), but that does not

INSULATING MATERIALS COMPARED

TYPE	R-VALUE/ INCH	DO IT YOUR- SELF?	WHERE USED	COST	CAUTIONS
U-F foam	4.8–5.4	No	Walls only	High	Questions as to shrink-age; choose contrac-tor carefully
Rigid plastic	3.6–5.9	Yes	Anywhere	Medium-high	Cover with gypsum board or other fire-retardant material
Blown cellulose	3.1–3.8	No	Walls and ceilings	Medium	Be sure of borax treat-ment; look for UL listing; watch for fly-by-night operators
Poured cellulose	3.0–3.6	Yes	Walls and ceilings	Low	Be sure of borax treat-ment; look for UL listing
Mineral wool batts or blankets	2.9–3.6	Yes	Anywhere	Low	Cover any vapor bar-rier to prevent fire hazard
Blown mineral wool	2.1–3.2	No	Walls	Medium	None
Perlite	2.6	Yes	Walls	Medium	None
Vermiculite	2.1	Yes	Walls	Medium	None

necessarily mean that ureaformaldehyde is a *better* insulator. As a matter of fact, it may be a poor choice, since there have been some questions raised about the efficacy of ureaformaldehyde, as mentioned later in this chapter.

DO-IT-YOURSELF MATERIALS. Any type of blow-in insulation is beyond the capabilities of the do-it-yourselfer. It takes expensive equipment and expert know-how to blow in insulation. Equipment rental is expensive. Therefore, the choices available to the do-it-yourselfer are as follows.

Mineral wool. There are two types of mineral wool: fiberglass and rock wool. Both are made by melting inorganic substances and forming them into fibers. Fiberglass, the most commonly used, is manufactured by heating sand (silica, the main ingredient in glass) and then spinning it into fibers. Rock wool is made by blowing air through molten slag or limestone and forming it into woolly fibers. The fibers are then formed into long rolls, called blankets, or shorter sec-tions, called batts. Sometimes they are chopped up into pellets, forming loose or pour insulation.

Mineral wool is the insulating material most commonly available and the choice of most insulators. It is easy to apply, and is almost indestructible, being immune to decay, insects, deterioration, and fire. The major manufacturers are Owens-Corning Fiberglas, Certain-Teed, and Johns-Manville.

Mineral-wool batts come in lengths of 4 or 8 feet. Blankets come in long rolls, the length depending on the thickness of the material. R-11, for example, comes in 60-foot rolls, while R-19 comes in 40-foot rolls. The thicker the material, the

Mineral-wool batts come in lengths of 4 or 8 feet. Batts are particularly useful in very thick dimensions such as the 9-inch R-30 illustrated here.

shorter the length. All the rolls contain approximately the same amount of total insulation, and cost about the same. It just takes more rolls of thicker insulation to cover the same area than it would to use thinner insulation (but, of course, you get more R-value per square foot).

The most available sizes are R-11, which is about 3½ inches thick, and R-19, which is about 6 inches thick. Many people still use these size designations instead of the R-factors.

Vapor barriers. Mineral-wool batts or blankets are made both with and without vapor barriers. The barriers are foil, kraft paper, plastic, or tar paper. Foil is most common, although kraft paper is also popular. The vapor barrier is intended to prevent moisture from infiltrating the insulation, where the moisture often condenses from the collision between warm and cold air. Wet insulation

Most of the vapor barriers found in insulation today are made of aluminum foil.

is of little value, and a vapor barrier of some sort is necessary to help prevent moisture penetration into the insulation itself.

When you are laying insulation into virgin areas, where no insulating material is present, a vapor barrier is a necessity. If insulation containing a vapor barrier is already in place, unfaced insulation (without a vapor barrier) is the choice. Two vapor barriers are almost as bad as none at all.

If you are adding more insulation to an attic, you should buy unfaced insulation. You may, however, have trouble finding it. In that event, the vapor barrier can be slashed or pulled off (see Chapter 7). You pay a little more for the vapor barrier you aren't using, but the cost is negligible.

Loose mineral-wool fill. This material is difficult to find, and has less R-value per inch than cellulose fill. It is, however, a far superior choice to untreated cellulose, which, as explained below, is a fire hazard.

Loose mineral wool can be blown in place by a contractor or poured out of bags. The most common application by the do-it-yourselfer is between walls. It can be poured into walls from some attics or from the top of the wall after removing the gypsum board or other covering material. (See Chapter 8 for details.) Mineral wool (or cellulose) fill can also be used in attics and is especially good for filling between joists when laying blankets on top (see Chapter 7).

Cellulose fiber. Cellulose insulation is made of paper, usually old newspapers ground up and treated. It is organic vegetable matter and flammable. When properly treated with chemicals, usually borax, it is safe and effective. It's R-value ranges from 3.0 to 3.8 per inch, and should be stated on the bag.

Cellulose fill is a popular choice of contractors for blown-in installation. It also comes in bags for pouring. Major manufacturers treat their cellulose properly, but with the boom in insulating materials, some smaller manufacturers may

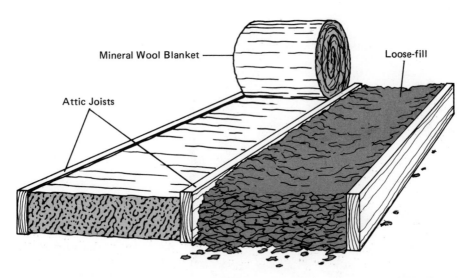

Mineral Wool Blanket

Loose-fill

Attic Joists

Insulation blankets or batts are preformed to a specified thickness. Loose-fill insulation, both fiberglass and cellulose, is poured in place, and may vary in thickness if not carefully installed.

skimp on the proper chemical treatment, which may constitute a fire hazard. Borax is also in short supply due to increased demand. Acceptable fire ratings are less than .25 or any of these three trade ratings: N-101-73; ASTM C-739-77; or HH-I-515 D. Avoid cellulose treated with aluminum sulfate. Although the R-ratings of different cellulose products are similar, some may have a higher R than others, so check specs on the bag. Many manufacturers give coverage instead of R-values per inch, so a little simple math may be necessary.

Cellulose fill is used for the same applications as loose mineral wool, but has a higher R-factor. Although blown cellulose has a lower R-factor than urea-formaldehyde foam, recent tests by the National Bureau of Standards have shown that the foam may shrink enough to lower its R-value to that of cellulose. See the discussion of ureaformaldehyde later in this chapter.

Rigid plastic foam. This is the same lightweight material often used in coffee cups, Christmas decorations, etc. It is easily cut and shaped to fit difficult spaces. For our purposes it comes in a wide variety of thicknesses, from ½ inch to 3 inches, and in sizes from 2×4-foot to 4×8-foot sheets. Polystyrene and Styrofoam (a modified brand styrene) are common foam materials. Rigid urethane is an excellent insulator, but is expensive and hard to find. Isocyanurate, best of all, is available as I write only as exterior sheathing.

Plastic foam has a closed-cell construction with millions of tiny air bubbles that are contained in such a way that little air passes through. It is an excellent insulator for that reason. Actually, Freon gas inhabits the bubbles in Styrofoam, which yields an R-factor of 5.4 per inch. The R-factor per inch varies from R-4.6 for polystyrene "beadboard" to R-9.0 for isocyanurate. Rigid foam is commonly used in refrigerators, ice chests, freezers, etc.

Rigid plastic foam, such as this tongue-and-groove Styrofoam, has a high R-value of 5.4 per inch and is excellent for new work such as the addition shown here.

Plastic foam is an excellent choice for tight areas, such as finished basements. It can be glued to the concrete with furring strips between. The finishing material can be nailed or cemented right on top. That way, the usual stud walls can be avoided, saving several inches of space all around, which can make the difference between having a usable pool table or not.

Using a special type of construction adhesive which will not attack the foam, rigid panels can be cemented to almost anything, including concrete. Make sure that the adhesive states it is suited for this use, however. Plastic foam cuts easily with a pocket or utility knife. All rigid plastic is flammable, and must be covered with ½-inch gypsum board.

Perlite and vermiculite. These are lightweight minerals that are often used as potting materials for plants. They are found in small bags in nurseries and garden shops. Both are relatively expensive and hard to find in large quantities. The R-value is not great, but these materials do not settle, and they filter well between obstacles such as wires, ducts, outlets, etc.

For special use in areas where access is difficult, you may want to use perlite or vermiculite, but other materials are better and cheaper for bigger jobs.

Other do-it-yourself materials. As we have seen in Chapter 4, most home-building materials are poor insulators. Glass and masonry are among the worst. So are most metals. There may be times when the standard insulating materials won't do, however. If you simply wish to cover up an area to keep out the wind, for example, wood is probably the best material. Of the various woods, particleboard and fir plywood have the best R-values for the money.

Polyethylene plastic is not an insulating material as such, but does make an effective vapor barrier. It is commonly used in 4-mil or 6-mil thickness to cover the ground in a crawl space. Unfaced insulation laid between studs or joists should be covered with a sheet of polyethylene stapled to the inside of the framing. This actually makes a better vapor barrier than the faced insulation, since the barrier in this case is continuous and also covers the framing.

CONTRACTOR-USED MATERIALS. As discussed in Chapter 8, between-the-wall insulation is difficult and messy for the homeowner, but can be accomplished by an insulating contractor. The price is pretty stiff compared to the jobs you can do yourself, but may still be worthwhile when you calculate the overall savings in fuel bills over the years.

Although it is impossible to give any concrete advice for particular homes in a given area, various studies indicate that blown-in cellulose is the best buy. Urea-formaldehyde (U-F) foam may yet prove to be better, but there have been some rather unsettling studies about some installations, as discussed later in this chapter.

Blown-in cellulose. This type of insulation is ideal for constructed walls which have little or no insulation. A typical 3½-inch "blow" offers about R-13 thermal resistance. Alternate choices for the do-it-yourselfer are unattractive. It is possible to remove all the plaster or wallboard and put in mineral-wool blankets, but the expense, time, and nuisance make this clearly silly. It is more feasible, but still difficult and messy, to remove a section of the wall covering at the top

Before blowing in cellulose or foam insulation, a row of shingles or siding is removed to gain access to the sheathing.

of each wall and pour insulation down through the studs (see Chapter 8). In addition to the problems of cutting and patching up, however, there is always the possibility that cross-bracing, wiring, heat ducts, or other obstacles will prevent the pour material from filling the entire wall.

Blown-in cellulose does require some covering material to be temporarily removed from the wall. Generally, this is done on the outside. One row of shingles or siding is removed, and a hole is drilled or punched through the sheathing. The cellulose fiber is then blown in through a hose into the entire area between the studs. One hole must be drilled into each framing cavity.

Siding or shingles are easily removed by the contractor and replaced without marring the looks of the exterior. Not every type of siding material, however, lends itself to exterior application. Plastic, aluminum, or steel siding is not read-

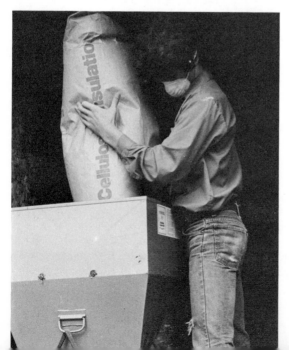

Bagged cellulosic fiber insulation is poured into a blowing machine.

Cellulose is blown from the machine shown on the previous page into the hose, which puts the fibers between the studs.

ily pulled out without destruction to the surface. In that case, the contractor may enter the wall through the inside. After the insulation is blown into an interior wall, a wooden plug is placed in the hole. The plug is then spackled over and the wall will need repainting or repairing.

In a typical blow-in cellulose installation, the bags of cellulose are poured into the mixer and carried through the hose into the nozzle. First the installer blows the cellulose into the bottom area, then up to the top portion. The force of the nozzle keeps filling up the between-frame area until no more can be added. As soon as the cellulose starts backing up to the hole, the hose is removed and inserted into the next area.

If there is some insulation already in the wall, the contractor pokes a hole through the other insulation and blows the cellulose through the insulation to

When the cellulose starts backing up and out the hole, the hose is withdrawn. The hole at left shows a filled-up cavity. New holes are drilled as each one is filled.

This hole punched in the wall shows that there is some mineral-wool insulation there, but not much. Cellulose will fill the cavity completely, pressing the mineral wool to the outside wall.

the inside of the wall. This presses the insulation against the outside of the wall and allows more room for the cellulose.

If there is no vapor barrier in place already, the cellulose is subject to moisture penetration. When properly treated, however, the cellulose is resistant to moisture and should not deteriorate or get soggy. To be on the safe side, however, it is recommended that paint for the inside walls be oil-based, which is a form of vapor barrier.

A blown-in cellulose job on all walls of an average house should be about $1000. A typical price is 50 cents per square foot. Many contractors, such as the Energy-Saver Insulation Corporation, which did the home shown in the photos, offer a warranty for the life of the structure. The warranty states that the fiber material is "permanently treated to resist fire, rodents, vermin, and moisture; that it will not pack or settle, and that its component parts will not deteriorate . . . " The warranty further states that "failure of our product or installation . . . will entitle owner to free replacement service."

Any contractor who does such work on your home should offer a similar warranty. The warranty, of course, is worthless if the firm goes out of business, so it pays to deal with well-known and reliable contractors. To play it safe, check the R-factors, fire resistance, and other data on the bags the contractor uses.

Blown-in cellulose is also used for attics and other areas. Most attics are easy enough to do yourself, so it ordinarily would not pay to have the contractor do that, too. If you are having the walls done, however, get a price from the contractor for doing the attic as well. It may be that he can do the extra work almost as cheaply as you can yourself. It is doubtful that it will pay to have a contractor blow in attic insulation alone.

Blown-in mineral wool. In general, blown-in cellulose is a better deal than blown-in mineral wool because you get more R-value per dollar. Local conditions do vary, though, so it is well to get a price from a mineral-wool installer to see for yourself. An audit by the Center for Energy Policy and Research (CEPR), New York Institute of Technology, Old Westbury, N.Y., found that mineral-wool installers charged only slightly to moderately more than cellulose

Cellulose is also blown into attic areas. For this, a larger hose nozzle is used.

contractors. However, the best R-factor you could get from a 3½-inch-thick blow would be 9.0, compared to about 13 for cellulose.

Mineral wool is blown in the same general way as cellulose. The chief advantage of mineral wool is that you don't have to worry about the material the way you do for cellulose. Mineral wool by its nature is resistant to fire, rodents, and vermin.

Ureaformaldehyde foam. U-F foam, as this product is usually called, has the highest R-factor of all available home-insulating materials. Furthermore, when properly installed, it effectively fills every nook and cranny in the wall, giving better coverage than any other. It is a relatively new product, however, and not fully field-tested.

U-F foam has been highly praised and recommended in many publications, but studies done in 1977 by the National Bureau of Standards (NBS) showed that the foam shrank 7.3 percent after 20 months, and continued to shrink thereafter. Manufacturers have agreed that some shrinkage would occur, but said that it would only be 2 to 3 percent.

Shrinking of the foam means that much of its insulating value is lost. Shrinkage of 10 percent or more would mean that its actual R-value would approximate that of cellulose. Furthermore, as it shrinks, foam is inclined to pull away from walls, and may split and crack, leaving passages for wind, air, and thermal loss.

At this writing, further testing is being conducted by the Energy Research and Development Administration (ERDA), which may resolve the controversy. Since U-F foam installations cost more than cellulose (50 percent more in the CEPR example), it seems wiser at this point to opt for cellulose.

Another problem with U-F is its use of chemicals. There is often an odor problem after its application, although it disappears quickly enough. U-F is recommended only between walls, also. The NBS warns against using foams in attics, where it may disintegrate in the high temperatures found there. Furthermore, U-F is made on the site by mixing chemicals with a catalyst and compressed air. It comes out of the nozzle like shaving cream. NBS warns that some formaldehyde gas may seep into the living areas, although it would not be especially dangerous. Nevertheless, with headlines blaring new problems each day concerning chemicals, I worry a bit about this product.

I discussed these questions with Bill Webb of the Conservation and Comfort Company of Bellmore, New York, who is also a member of the insulation association. He says that the alleged problems stem from a rash of fly-by-night operators who buy inexpensive equipment and go to work with little or no experience. Proper equipment, he says, costs $25,000, while some installers pay $5000 or less. According to Mr. Webb, it takes a certain amount of skill and know-how to do a proper job. Their company has had very few complaints of odor or shrinkage. He urges that anyone considering using U-F foam choose a qualified, experienced contractor. Good advice.

BUYING GUIDELINES. In the early part of 1978, prices for all insulating materials were high and probably headed higher. But insulation is still a bargain compared to the cost of fuel.

Price differentials between the various types of materials are generally insignificant. In terms of R-value per dollar, the costs of mineral wool and cellulose are approximately the same as of this writing. Plastic foam is a little higher, but not that much.

I hope that by the time you read this, shortages will have eased and prices will stabilize, if not get lower. Unfortunately, the capacities of insulating manufacturers are not expected to increase fast enough to offset the surge in demand.

Therefore, there are only a few words of wisdom for those who are buying insulation at this time:

• First and foremost, insulate your home as close to the local recommendations as possible. This is the best way to ensure the most value for your dollar. Whatever you pay will be reimbursed eventually in lower fuel costs.

• Since prices between the several types are similar per R-value, your main consideration should be the suitability of the material to the type of insulation. Pour cellulose may be a little cheaper, but mineral-wool blankets are easier to lay in an attic, under floors, and in crawl spaces. For use between walls, cellulose is about all the do-it-yourselfer has to choose from. Rigid plastic foam is easier and quicker for basements, foundations, and other exterior uses. It is also best where space is limited. You'll pay a little more, though, per square foot of R-value.

• In truth, you may have to settle for what is locally available, regardless of cost or use.

• When using a contractor, have him give you a written estimate. He can tell you the cost per R-value, or you can easily compute it yourself. Choose your contractor carefully, especially with U-F foam. Check all cellulose bags for fire rating as explained earlier in this chapter.

• Work out your own payback periods, using the method explained in Chapters 4 and 5, before signing up for any contractor-applied job.

7 | How to Insulate Ceilings

OF THE MANY energy-saving steps possible in your home, none is more important than insulating the ceiling. This is true in all parts of the country—indeed, the world—because there will always be days when the home will be either too cold or too hot for comfort. Ceiling insulation is most important in cooler climates, because heated air rises and escapes through the roof. But it is also vital in warmer regions, since on hot days, heat builds up in the attic and penetrates downward, making the rooms below too hot. Remember, heat doesn't just go up—it always flows toward cooler areas, regardless of direction.

Ceiling insulation also provides a thermal barrier for cool air when the rooms below are air conditioned. In warmer climates, the energy savings can be just as great as for heated homes in cooler areas. As a matter of fact, many experts recommend ceiling insulation of R-38 for centrally air-conditioned homes regardless of location.

Homes in regions where heat is more of a problem than cold often have different problems than those in colder parts of the country. Flat-roofed and one-story homes are often built without attic space, and conventional insulating techniques do not apply; the proper techniques are explained later in this chapter.

However, in most inhabited parts of the world, homes are built with some sort of attic space. For most of us, "ceiling" insulating means "attic" insulation. The attic may be a large, roomy one, as in older homes, where you can walk around and even build extra rooms. Newer homes are usually built with just a small enclosed area over the top floor, where there is barely room to stand in the center.

The size of the attic space does not affect the insulating technique. The big difference here is whether there is a floor or not. If there is no floor, the insulating job is quite simple. If you have a floor, you must decide whether you will be using the attic space as living area, now or in the future. We'll get into that later.

THE UNFLOORED ATTIC. Luckily for most of us, modern attics are usually unused and unfloored. It is a simple matter for the do-it-yourselfer to insulate such an attic.

How much insulation to add depends on what you already have and on local conditions. If you haven't studied Chapters 4 and 5, do so now and determine the ideal R-level for your home.

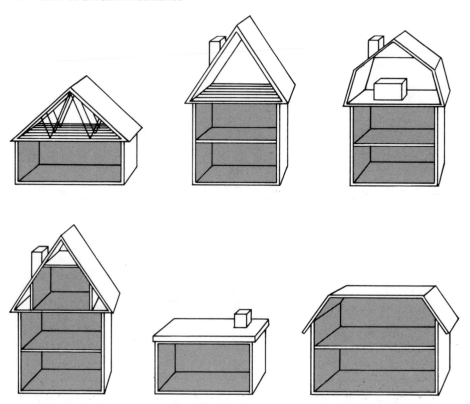

The usual place to insulate a ceiling is from the attic. But there are lots of types of attics, as illustrated, and some houses which do not have attics at all. The shaded areas are those that should be insulated.

Blanket or batt mineral-wool insulation is the choice of most people for attic insulation. To find out how much you need, simply find the area of the attic by measuring the perimeters of the rooms below and multiplying the length by the width. In most cases, the attic area is the same as that of the floor below. Some houses may have slight variations, but it isn't worthwhile to go into the attic and measure there. You'll have a difficult time getting exact measurements in the low perimeter areas, and you'll have to keep shifting boards around to keep from falling between the joists. If your measurements are a little off and you buy too much or too little insulation, it's usually no problem to purchase a little more, or take back an unused roll or package for a refund or credit. Unlike wallpaper and paint, there are no subtle differences in batch colors to worry about.

Preparation. In addition to the insulating materials, you'll need a folding rule or metal tape for measuring, a sharp knife for cutting the insulation, some long, strong planks to stand or kneel upon, and a long stick for poking the insulation into corners. A trouble light or some other sort of illumination is also a must. Get one with a long extension so you can move it around, or use sev-

Gloves and loose-fitting clothes are required dress for attic insulation. Goggles are recommended, though in warm attics perspiration may interfere with vision. A hard hat is a good idea when roofing nails stick through the sheathing.

eral of them. If the insulation is thick, also bring up a serrated butcher knife.

For your safety and comfort, wear cotton gloves, a long-sleeved loose-fitting shirt, and other clothes that expose as little of your skin as possible. Mineral wool can be very irritating to the body. (It's similar to what is used in the itching powder.) If you have allergies or respiratory problems you should wear a surgical-type mask, since the fibers can irritate throat or lungs. It's a good idea, too, to wear goggles to prevent eye irritation, but attic insulating is a sweaty job even on cold days, and goggles are bound to steam up. It's better to see where you're going, particularly since you won't be working overhead.

Since getting up and down out of the attic can be tiring, if not downright exhausting, it's best to push all the rolls up through the access door before you start. They may not fit through easily, but squeezing them through won't do them any harm. Roll them or shove them as far as possible at first, to make room for subsequent ones. Whatever you do, don't open the rolls before you get them into the attic, because they'll be very awkward to handle. If the rolls come in packages of four, however, you'll probably have to unwrap the outer covering to get them through the access hole. You may want to wear goggles for this job, because you'll be doing most of the shoving overhead.

You should also push up all the boards and tools before you pull yourself up into the attic. Attach all the lights and extensions and extend them as far as you can into the attic. When you're sure everything is ready, haul your body up into the attic, and you're ready to begin.

Shove the loose end of the blanket toward the edge until it meets the rafters. Leave a few inches at the end for air rising through eave vents.

Choose a corner in which to begin, and lay out your boards ahead of you to form a walkway. Try not to let too much board extend unsupported over any joist, because you're bound to step on that and become the unwitting principal in a situation comedy. Lay out several boards where you'll be working, but not too close to the eaves, where there is very little headroom. And be careful of the ends of nails sticking through the roof. Keep your head below the rafters whenever possible to avoid scalping yourself. Wear a hard hat if you foresee this as a problem.

When there is no insulation. If you have no insulation already there, you will be laying the batts or blankets between the joists. Starting in one corner of the attic, face the package or roll in the direction you'll be working. Cut open roll-insulation covering with your knife and pull or cut through the paper strips that are wrapped around the outside. The insulation will then unravel in the right direction.

Take the loose end of the roll and shove it toward the eave. Don't try to walk it down to the edge, but grasp it a few feet back and push it forward until it meets the rafters. Don't cram it in, since a little room should be left for air circulation from the eaves up to the ridge. There should be at least some overhang, so that you will more than adequately cover the ceilings below. If there are vents in the eaves, be sure not to cover them up. Install baffles, if necessary.

The insulation should fit rather tightly between the joists, so gently push

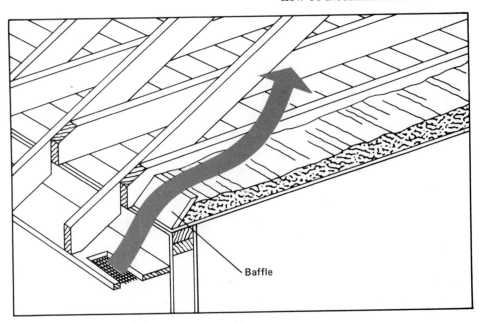

Install baffles as shown if there are eave vents.

Use a long stick to press the insulation into place where you can't reach it. Don't press so hard that you compress it.

Fit insulation carefully around such obstructions as wires and bridging. Cut the blankets and work around the obstacle if necessary.

down on it until it hits the ceiling wallboard. Use your long stick to accomplish this at the edge where you have difficulty reaching. Don't compress the material too much, though, or you destroy the effectiveness.

When the end of the roll is in place, keep unrolling it until you reach the other side, or the end of the roll. If the roll extends beyond the other edge, measure the distance to the other edge and cut the roll off there. To cut the insulation, place your utility knife on the foil or paper side with a board underneath. Cut through as far as possible. It should be very easy to cut the vapor barrier. Cutting the mineral wool is not difficult, either, but may take several passes because of the thickness. If you are laying very thick insulation, you should find it easier to make the first cut through the vapor barrier with the utility knife, then finish the job with a serrated butcher knife.

Lay the cut edge over to the eaves on the other side as you did in the beginning, smoothing down with your hands and a stick at the edge. Try to get the insulation under and around any wiring or other obstructions. You may have to cut the insulation to work around bridging, pipes, etc. You don't need the hands of a brain surgeon for this, and the natural resiliency of the material makes patching easy, too. Do make the cuts as accurately as possible, and fit the insulation around the obstructions tightly. Make sure that the insulation stops about 3 inches from the edge of any recessed fixtures or other heat producers. Use only noncombustible materials, such as unfaced blankets, between chimney and framing.

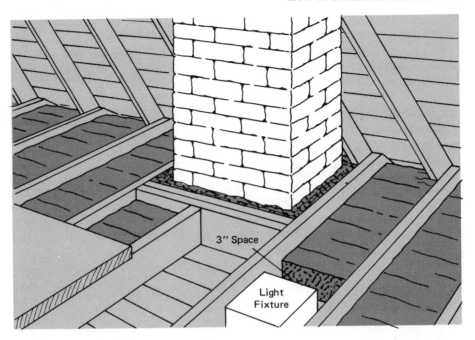

Always keep insulation at least 3 inches away from light fixtures. Use scraps of un-faced insulation between chimneys and framing.

Whenever the roll runs out, simply let it stop where it is and start another roll. Make sure that the ends fit snugly together, however. Keep working like this across the entire attic, moving your boards as necessary, until you finish the job—or until your knees give out. Since most of the job will be on your knees, it's a good idea to go back to the center once in a while to stretch them out. Or go back downstairs occasionally for a breather. Though this isn't a hard job, it is time-consuming, and you won't be able to work too long at a stretch in such a cramped, hot, and dusty atmosphere. Better to take a break once in a while and have a beer than to become overtired and step between the joists, winding up downstairs when you least expect it.

There is very little difference if you use batts instead of blankets. You will just do a little more fitting where batts butt together.

Double layers of insulation will be required in most parts of North America. R-22 insulation (if you can find it) will usually bring you up to the top of the joists, unless your joists are unusually wide. Thicknesses as great as R-30 and R-38 are manufactured but not too readily available. Furthermore, insulation laid only between the joists allows thermal loss through the joists themselves. It is better to cover the joists with a second layer of insulation laid at right angles to the bottom layer than to use one very thick blanket.

R-factors are additive. Instead of using one R-30 roll, for example, you can lay one layer of R-19 and one of R-11, and they will have the same effective-ness as R-30. If you cross over the joists with the second layer, you actually

CORRECT   **INCORRECT**

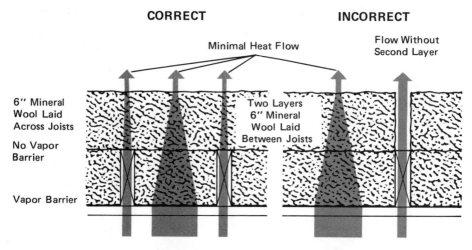

Minimal Heat Flow

Flow Without
Second Layer

6" Mineral
Wool Laid
Across Joists

Two Layers
6" Mineral
Wool Laid
Between Joists

No Vapor
Barrier

Vapor Barrier

Because of the relatively low R-factor of wood, there is considerable heat loss through the joists of a ceiling. Laying a second layer of insulation at right angles to the joists greatly reduces this thermal loss.

get a better overall result than using one layer of R-30 with joists uncovered.

To achieve R-30, get one layer of R-19, which should come almost up to the top of the joists. This layer should contain a vapor barrier. Using unfaced rolls of R-11, lay a second blanket in the opposite direction to the first. For R-32, use R-19 with vapor barrier for the first, and R-13 unfaced above. For R-38, use two rolls of R-19, with vapor barrier below and unfaced on top.

The second layer of unfaced insulation is put down just as you would if there were already insulation in place as described below.

When there is already some insulation installed. If you have some insulation but not enough to provide sufficient thermal resistance for your area, a second layer is laid on top of the first. If the R-value recommended is low, you can place the second layer on top of the first between the joists.

If the R-value recommended is more than R-22, however, the second layer should be placed at right angles to the first, as explained above. This can lead to some minor difficulties. Suppose, for example, there is only R-7 or R-11 in the attic, and you want to bring the total up to R-30. The available sizes may not add up to the total R-value you desire. With R-7 already there, for example, and R-33 recommended, you have to find batts or blankets rated at R-26. It may be that somebody makes that thickness, but you'll have a rough time finding it. Also, if you crisscross the second layer, it'll sag between the joists. (This won't affect the R-value, but may waste a few inches per roll.)

One way to solve this is to fill the gap with bags of loose fill. You can't be as scientific with pouring material, because there will be minor variations in depth. But putting a layer of loose pour between the layers also helps fill the gaps that are otherwise left by obstructions and butting of batts and blankets. It also gives a nice, even surface on which to lay the second layer.

In my house, for example, the contractor had laid R-11 in the attic. The rec-

Before adding more insulation, fix up the old materials. Where insulation crosses on top of wiring, cut through the insulation (top photo) and work it underneath the wires.

I found only R-11 in my ceiling, which left considerable space between the top of the insulation and the top of the joists, so I decided to fill the spaces with pour cellulose.

ommended ceiling value was R-30 to R-33. Since Long Island summers can be very hot, and we had room air conditioners below, it would not be unreasonable to insulate up to R-38. About the only type of unfaced insulation that was available at the time was R-19. I could've laid that on top of the R-11, but I decided that I would fill up the between-joists area with cellulose before I laid the second layer of R-19. The manufacturer of the cellulose rated his product at R-4 per inch, but that struck me as a little high. I used an average per the NBS and figured R-3.5 per inch. If I laid 2 inches, roughly, on top of the R-11, that would give me an R-7 for the cellulose (approximately). The cellulose would reach about to the top of the joists, so that I could lay unfaced R-19 blankets on top without any big dips between. And I'd have a total R-value of about R-37, more than adequate for heating and just about right for A/C.

You will have to work out your own mathematics to get the optimum R for your house, but it should not be difficult if and when more sizes and types of insulation are available. If you can't get what you want, use cellulose between, as I did.

As discussed above, the second layer of insulation should always be without vapor barrier. But what do you do if you can't find the unfaced type? It's not that big a problem. The usual recommendation is to slash the vapor barrier in many places so as to render it inoperative. With foil-faced insulation, however, it seems easier to simply pull the vapor barrier off. You may loose a smidgin of mineral wool this way (it tends to stick to the foil), but not enough to worry about. It is probably easier to slash other vapor barriers, however. Either way, you're accomplishing the purpose—preventing moisture from accumulating between vapor barriers.

Unfaced R-19 blankets went on top of the cellulose. After cutting the paper covering, slash or pull off the gummed tape.

Start the first row of the second layer butted against the bottom of the rafters, beginning in one corner. Use boards or plywood to provide a kneeling or sitting surface.

After one roll runs out, simply butt the next roll snugly against the end of the first.

Just roll out the unfaced insulation along the edge of the first blanket.

A serrated knife cuts through unfaced insulation quickly. Enough is left over to tuck over the top plate of the gable wall below.

The end of the insulation is tucked over the top plate.

The completed job. Lots of energy and fuel dollars will be saved now.

If unfaced insulation isn't available, you can use faced insulation, but the vapor barrier must be slashed, as shown, to let moisture pass through.

You lay additional unfaced insulation the same as you lay that with a vapor barrier, except that it is laid across, rather than between, the joists. Again, you start in a corner, but lay the rolls or batts at right angles to the previous insulation. This time, the side of the insulation is pressed against the juncture of the joists and rafters. It won't extend as far as the original layer, but that's okay. As you will recall, there should be an air passage anyway from the eaves to the ridges.

Before you begin, though, check out the original installation. Chances are that the original contractor wasn't as careful as you would've been. In my case, the contractor hadn't bothered to weave the insulation around obstructions. Whenever the insulation hit any wiring, for example, the batts just went on top. I had to slice the insulation around the wires—not any big deal, but a comment on the conscientiousness of contractors. (Be careful not to cut into the wiring.) If there are any gaps in the old insulation, fill as best as possible before adding the new.

Once you've prepared the area properly and laid the first roll, the rest should go easily enough. Since the joists usually run across the shorter dimension, you should be able to make long runs with the across-joist insulation. Butt the next roll against the first, and continue the same way until you get to the center.

When you get to the center, approximately under the ridge board, or top point of the house, it is easier to begin anew on the other side and work back again toward the center. Otherwise, you will have to crawl across the newly laid insulation to get to the other edge, or work out some other awkward way to get to the other side. If you wind up with less than a regular width in the center, you will have to cut a piece to fit in the center. It's easier there, though,

It is quicker to pull off the vapor barrier than to slash it, although you should take care not to pull off too much insulation adhering to the barrier.

than under the eaves. A serrated knife is the best tool for cutting unfaced insulation. If you miss the mark and leave gaps, it's easy to fill in with scraps. Don't worry about cutting the piece too wide. Insulation is easily squashed to fill any given space. (But don't go overboard and crush too much.)

When I reinsulated my attic, I noticed that there was no insulation at all in the space between the top plate and the end joist. Therefore, as shown in the photos, I ran the crisscross insulation down onto the top plate. This meant that I often had to slash the insulating material to fit around the studs at each gable end. It's easy enough, though, and provides a little bit of extra insulation at the top of the sidewalls.

Other methods of increasing ceiling insulation. Pour cellulose or mineral wool may also be added to attics to bring the insulation up to the desired R-level. This is generally most effective when only a few more Rs are needed. You can also use it, however, between two layers of batts or blankets, as I did. Cellulose is good for adding to poor or damaged insulation, and for additions to insulation that is already near the joist tops, so that you can also cover the wood.

There are no special problems with this type of insulation except for keeping an even surface. It is simply poured out of the bag and leveled with a board or rake to the desired depth. So that you don't go too far off in your depth perception, you can string a line level here and there at the proper height. Or take measurements every few square feet to make sure that you're getting it reasonably level. Observe the cautions detailed in Chapter 6 when buying cellulose, particularly as regards fire retardance.

Blown-in insulation can also be used, of course, but this is not a do-it-yourself job. See Chapter 6 for more about contractor-applied insulation. You will usually find that you can lay blanket insulation at considerably less cost.

Other methods, such as those used below for floored attics, can also be used, but they don't make much sense unless you *have* to use them. One exception might be lowering the downstairs ceilings if they are much too high anyway.

THE FLOORED ATTIC. As discussed at the beginning of this chapter, the homeowner is confronted with several choices when the attic is already floored. In most cases, the floor will have been laid by a previous owner for a reason. The attic was probably planned for future living space or for greater ease of storage. Not always, though—in many older homes, it was simply the thing to do when lumber and labor were cheap. In virtually all cases, however, the insulation under the floorboards will be either very thin or nonexistent—usually the latter.

To find out for sure, find a loose floorboard, or loosen one if they're all nailed down. Check underneath, using a flashlight if necessary. If you find some insulation, check for an R-number, and measure if you can't find any. Chances are overwhelming that any insulation there will be woefully inadequate. Now you have a few more questions to answer.

Does the floor serve a useful function? Do you use the attic frequently for storage? What kind of floor is it? Sometimes people just slap a few boards down to provide a walkway. At other times—usually long ago—the attic floor may have been just as carefully laid as the other floors. The answers to these questions will determine your next choice—whether or not you want to leave the flooring there.

Mineral wool can also be blown into the attic. Although one of least R-effective methods, the material is safe and can be applied quickly.

If the flooring is good and well laid, it is difficult and wasteful to rip it up. But suppose the insulation is thin or nonexistent? What do you do then? That involves another choice. There are several things you can do. You *can* rip the flooring up, but you've already decided that this is not a happy choice. You can lay insulation over the floorboards if you wish. This is a possibility if you conclude that you'll rarely use the space even for storage. The solution to the dilemma in many cases is to insulate the roof itself. This is easy and relatively inexpensive to do, but you won't get the full benefit of the insulation because much heat will be lost in the unused attic area itself. Nonetheless, many people take this course, which is certainly better than having no insulation at all.

One solution is to have insulation blown under the floor by a contractor. It is worthwhile, in any case, to have an estimate done to see what cost and trade-offs will be. There is one more possibility, though, for those with high-ceilinged, older homes. That is to construct false ceilings in the rooms below by putting up new framing at a lower level and attaching the insulation to that. There are a couple of ways of doing this. It can be a costly and time-consuming project, but you receive a dual benefit this way. Not only will you provide much-needed insulation, but you'll eliminate a great deal of wasted heat which collects in the unused extra space above the usual ceiling height.

It is also possible to use rigid plastic foam on the ceilings below. This is more expensive than conventional methods, and is usually unacceptable in modern homes because the ceilings are about as low as possible already. This method is ideal, however, for cathedral ceilings, as explained later in this chapter.

If you don't expect to be using the attic for living or storage, the insulation can simply be laid down on top of the existing floorboards. If there is no insulation under the floorboards, use blankets with vapor barrier attached, and simply roll them out over the floor, tightly butted. If there is already some insulation,

The simplest and least expensive way of insulating an attic with a finished floor is to lay batts over the floorboards. This, of course, makes the insulated area unusable for storage or living area.

use unfaced rolls in the same manner. This work goes very fast, because there is no stapling or crawling around on temporary boards or joists. If you change your mind later, the insulation can easily be rolled back up again and reused.

If partitions have been erected in the attic, you'll have to get behind them and install the insulation in the other areas that aren't floored behind partitions. Otherwise, heat will escape through these other areas.

If you wish to retain a small space for storage, it should not be too much of a job to pry up the boards in one small section near the access door and put insulation between the joists in the standard way. Reinstall boards when you're done.

If you'd like to use the attic for storage but don't expect to convert it to living space, the best solution is to have cellulose blown in by experts. A reputable contractor will completely fill all the spaces between the floorboards and the ceiling below with his product, and this should produce an R-factor of from 20 to 25, depending on the material and skill of application. You may find thicker joists than the usual 6 inches in some homes, particularly older homes, so that when the space is filled in with blown-in insulation, the R-value can be 30 or higher.

When you expect to use the attic area for living space someday, the insulating itself is easy. But that's only part of the problem. The insulation has to be attached to something, and that's where the trouble begins. Now you've got to put up some framing—unless you're lucky and a previous owner or a generous contractor has already done it for you.

Framing isn't really a difficult job, but it's got to be done right. If you realize that, at least in this instance, the main job of the framing is to provide nailing surfaces for the finish material, you'll have an easier time of it. You don't have to decide now what type of finish material you'll be using. If you use the usual framing "centers," any type of finish material can be used at a later date.

BUILDING AN ATTIC ROOM. In the attic, some of the framing will already have been done for you. Overhead collar beams that hold the rafters from shifting should have been installed about every third rafter. These will help form your ceiling. You'll also be using part of the rafters as part of your usual sloping "ceiling-walls." Unless your house is very old or is an unusual shape, the rafters and beams will be on 16-inch centers, which will also be the centers for your framing.

It is best to envision exactly what type of attic room (or rooms) you want before you begin to frame. For example, will the area be a study, a studio, or simply bedrooms? Will there be other partitions? Will there be a bathroom there? If you're putting in bedrooms—the usual usage—do you want to build in storage space under the eaves? That will make a difference when you put in the insulation.

Not all of us can think that far in advance, though, and if you haven't got an exact idea, then just proceed to put up the outside framing and insulate that. You can always make adjustments later.

Begin by determining where you want the short knee walls to be located. These walls are framed by putting up short dwarf studs between the rafters and the attic floor. The first step is to install a sole plate across the floor where the wall will be. Use either 2×3 or 2×4 lumber for all the framing. At the ends of each sole plate, attach studs from the top of the plate to the rafters above. Drop a plumb line to determine where to nail the stud. Toenail to the sole plate,

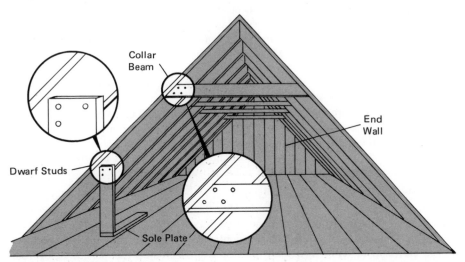

The collar beams are the overhead framing between rafters. For framing the attic, additional collar beams are added to form a complete ceiling. A sole plate forms the bottom of the knee walls. Dwarf studs are nailed from the sole plate to the rafters to complete the framing for the knee walls.

Batts are stapled to the collar beams, in this case R-30 High-R Fiberglas. Goggles should be worn when working overhead to keep the glass fibers out of the eyes.

then use a spirit level to plumb the stud. Nail through the top of the stud into the rafter.

When both end studs have been nailed up, run a chalkline from the juncture of the stud and rafter at one end to the same spot at the other end. Now nail up the remaining dwarf studs to form your knee wall, using your level to keep them all plumb. Do the same for the other side.

The ceiling will be the same height as the collar beams. Check the beams to make sure they are all the same height. If not, take the lowest one and use that for your ceiling height. Measure the same height from the floor at all rafters and nail 2×3s or 2×4s wherever there are no collar beams installed already. Any collar beams that are not level can now be shimmed out with thin pieces of lumber to the same height as the others.

There may be more to the framing than that, depending on what you intend to do with the room. If you plan to finish the walls, you should put horizontal nailers where the collar beams join the roof joists and where the roof joists join the knee-wall studs. For the moment, though, you've done all you have to do to provide the insulation, which is the main job at the moment.

Attaching the insulation. Blankets or batts of mineral wool with attached vapor barrier are best for this type of work. Use the recommended R-values for walls and ceilings in your region. Treat the sloping ceiling area as a regular ceiling except that your space is limited to the depth of the rafters, plus about ¾-inch air space above. And don't forget the unfloored area outside the perimeter of your walls (same R-value as the ceiling). The only tools needed are a staple gun and a utility knife. Since you'll be working overhead part of the time, you should really try to use goggles to protect your eyes, although you may find that they interfere too much with vision if you get them sweated up. A thick cap or hard-

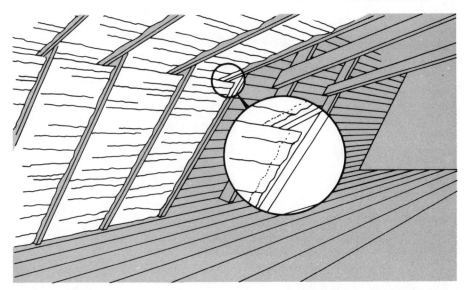

Don't try to run continuous blankets across the ceiling and down the sloping walls. The attic construction shown results in an offset, as shown in the circle. Start a new run where the sloping part begins.

hat is also advised when working overhead, as is a mask if you have respiratory problems.

The vapor barrier in all cases should face the interior, or warm side, of the room. Starting with a corner of the ceiling beams, insert a staple into each side of one end of the insulation. There are two ways of stapling the vapor barrier. The easier way is to put the staples into the sides of the framing, but then the vapor barrier doesn't cover the wood. The wood should then be covered with special tape. If you staple the vapor barrier to the framing front, you get a continuous vapor barrier, though you may also be left with bumps or bulges that will interfere with smooth application of the finish materials. Try it both ways and see which works best for you.

If you're working alone, line up the roll of insulation behind you and support the free length partially with your head as you work. A helper who can roll out and hold up the blanket makes it easier. Insert staples every 6 inches or so, working backward until you reach the other end of the ceiling beam. Cut the insulation to size with your utility knife and staple up that end. Proceed to the next beam until the whole ceiling is covered.

Next, do the sloping part of the ceiling. There will be an offset where the ceiling beams meet the rafters, so you'll have to do the sloping sections separately from the ceiling. These are stapled up in the same way as the ceiling.

Using the same insulation, make sure that all areas of the attic floor *outside* the framing are covered. Where there is no flooring, place the insulation between the joists as described in this chapter. If there is flooring behind your knee walls, you won't be using it, so simply lay the insulation on top of the flooring there. Remove or slash the vapor barriers if there is already some insulation with a vapor barrier.

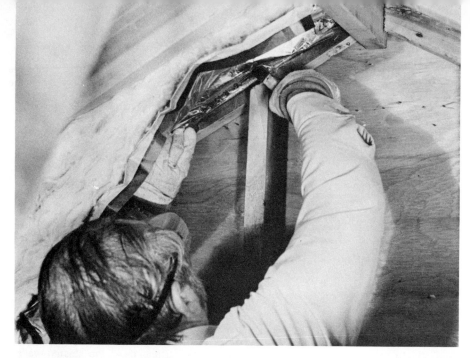

When there isn't enough headroom to form a new ceiling along the collar beams, the rafters can be insulated directly.

The walls of your new room are done last, using the same techniques as described for walls in the next chapter. After the whole job is done, tape over any tears in the vapor barrier and apply thin strips of polyethylene or weatherstripping tape over any uncovered framing to ensure against moisture condensation.

INSULATING ROOFS AND END WALLS. In some instances, it may be preferable to insulate a floored attic along the rafters and end walls. This is true where trusses interfere or where the collar beams are low and the usable space small. Such space will be used for storage rather than living area, because the trusses or collar beams will interfere with any useful living space.

To insulate the rafters, run batts or blankets from the ridge board to the eaves. The same methods are used as for applying insulation to the slanting roof of the framed-in room previously described. The end walls are done like any other wall (see next chapter). The insulation will have to be shaped to fit up into the peaks and along the slanted rafters.

INSULATING THE FINISHED ATTIC. If your attic area is already finished off, the odds are very high that it needs insulation. It may be difficult to check, however. The hand-on-the-wall test is one way, but the only positive method is by getting behind the walls and ceiling. There may be some sort of access door, or perhaps you have chests or shelving built into the knee walls which can be pulled out.

If there is no way of getting into the unfinished area, you may as well make an entrance of some kind, since it can also be used when you install the insulation. Use a keyhole or saber saw to cut into the ceiling material in such a way that you can make a trap door afterward.

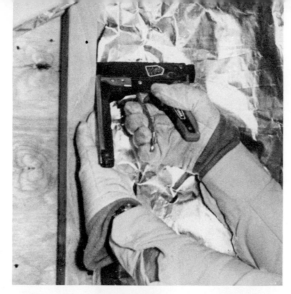

With a low ceiling, start the end-wall insulation right at the ridge board.

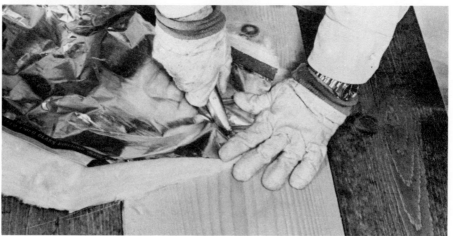

Cut the insulation precisely for a tight fit along the gable ends.

Boost yourself into the area above the ceiling and take a look at what's up there. It may be possible to move across the joists to the other open areas behind the walls. If not, more trap doors may be necessary. It's difficult to give exact directions on this, because of the many different ways an attic can be walled off.

In any case, the attic area should be insulated in the following places:

- ceiling
- sloping rafters above living space
- end walls
- *either* knee walls and outer attic floors, *or* outer rafters

If access is very difficult in any of the places, a contractor is probably your best bet. On the other hand, if you can get at most of these places yourself, then you can also install the insulation yourself.

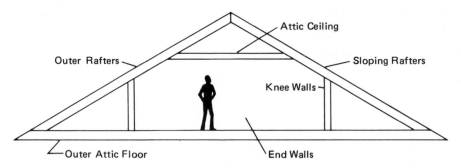

When the attic area is already finished off, but not insulated, these are the places where you'll have to go to work, if you have access. Do the attic ceiling, sloping rafters, and end walls. You have your choice of doing the knee walls *and* outer attic floors, or the outer rafters.

The ceiling should be covered with batts or blankets in the same way as other attic areas as described above. The sloping ceiling-walls and end walls may require the services of a contractor, unless you have room to provide rigid foam inside. You can also use the other methods of wall insulation described in the next chapter.

If you have access into the space behind the knee walls, you have an option. It is simpler and requires less materials to insulate the rafters above the unused areas with blankets or batts. These are installed the same way as for walls (see next chapter), and here it's best to staple the vapor barrier to the edge of the rafters because you don't have to worry about finishing materials over them. Insulating the rafters, however, in effect means that you're heating the unused space below. If the area is small, and you might use it for storage, this can be okay. When the area is large, however, too much heat may be wasted, and you are better off insulating just the knee walls (like any other walls) and the joists outside of the knee walls. The outer joists are insulated just as are any other ceiling joists. You will use a little more insulation this way, but save in the long run with a small reduction in heating costs. Any uninsulated areas should be vented just as you would vent a completely unused attic.

As long as you've cut holes in the ceiling and/or knee walls, you may as well use them for trap doors. The unused attic area can be used for storage, and may come in handy for roof or other repairs. Insulate the backs of the trap doors and put up some molding around them. A ceiling trap can simply rest on the molding, but you'll probably want to put hinges on the side doors, or perhaps use duct tape to hold them in place.

INSULATING TRAP DOORS. An oft-overlooked source of thermal loss is the "scuttle hole," or trap door, leading to the attic. Insulating the trap door is a little trickier than some other jobs, but not really difficult.

At least one edge of blanket mineral wool can be attached to the top of the door by folding the flange over the edge and stapling it. Since the next section will butt against the first, you won't be able to get at the flanges, so use construction adhesive to attach the rest of the insulation. An easier and neater method is to

The trap door should be as well insulated as the ceiling.

use rigid plastic for the job, if you have some around, but it isn't worthwhile to buy a big piece of foam for just this one little job.

INSULATING THE CEILING BELOW. In some areas of the country flat roofs are common. The average flat roof is not designed to withstand heavy layers of snow, so its use is usually confined to the Southwest, the Deep South, and commercial buildings in the rest of the country. Most homes need a roof that slants down to let the snow slide off.

If a home is built in that part of the country that never gets snow, it is axiomatic that the same home most probably will be air-conditioned in order for its inhabitants to survive. Although various devices are used to reflect the heat off a roof, plenty of energy loss occurs.

Those who don't want to, or can't, use any of the methods above to insulate their attics, for whatever reason, have a problem similar to those with flat roofs.

A flat roof requires different insulating techniques, none of them easy or cheap.

The technique for insulating flat roofs, mansard roofs, or floored roofs where no other method will do is usually the same: so insulate from below.

Rigid plastic foam is the simplest and most R-efficient material for insulating ceilings from below. This method works equally well for flat roofs, cathedral ceilings, or other applications. Plastic foam comes in large sheets in widths from ½ inch to 3 inches.

Polystyrene foam, often called beadboard or by one brand name, Styrofoam, is attached to the ceiling by means of special construction adhesive that comes in cartridges and is applied with a caulking gun.

Plastic foam is not in itself flammable in the usual sense of the word, but it does tend to melt and disintegrate, making it a fire hazard. It must, therefore, be covered. The foam itself is very easy to apply, but you must remember to provide nailing or gluing surfaces for the minimum ½-inch gypsum board. Check manufacturer's instructions to determine whether the drywall can be glued directly to the foam on ceilings.

The easiest way to provide nailing surfaces is to intersperse the foam boards with furring strips, as illustrated in Chapter 9 for basement walls. The size of the furring depends on the thickness of the rigid foam. The ¾-inch foam used for the basement in the illustrations mentioned above is especially made for standard 1×3 furring. This thickness, however, is not enough for most ceiling applications. For 2-inch-thick foam, use furring a trifle thicker than the foam. Put the furring around all the edges and on 24-inch centers. Run furring across the joists on ceilings. Cut the foam with a sharp knife to fit between the furring, unless it comes precut to fit between furring as does the foam used in the basement photos in Chapter 9. For ceilings, use drywall nails to hold the foam in place until the mastic sets.

A mansard roof is often found on homes in the Colonial or French Provincial style. Insulating methods for ceilings are similar to those for flat roofs.

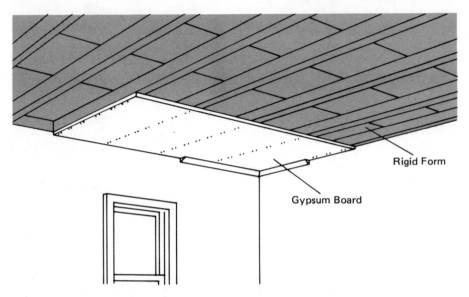

Rigid Form

Gypsum Board

Plastic foam is an excellent material for insulating a flat roof from below. All plastic foam must be covered by ½-inch gypsum board as shown.

When the foam and furring are all applied, cover with ½-inch gypsum board. Plastic foam acts as a pretty good vapor barrier itself, so no separate barrier is needed.

Dropped ceilings. This is another way to insulate ceilings from below. As discussed above, this method will also eliminate a lot of expensive-to-heat dead air space when there are high ceilings.

The simplest way to install a dropped ceiling is to hang aluminum channels, which are sold by a number of ceiling-material manufacturers. You may be able to find preinsulated ceiling panels. (Owens-Corning makes them, for one.) If not, mineral-wool batts can be laid on top of chickenwire hung on the wiring which holds up the gridwork. Lash the chickenwire to the vertical wires in sections, then slide in the insulation, vapor-barrier side down. For the last section, place the insulation on top of the chickenwire first, then attach it to the vertical wiring in one section. Plastic foam can also be placed on top of the ceiling panels.

You can also use standard wood framing to make a whole new ceiling. Nail 2×4 plates to all four walls into the studs, then toenail 2×4 joists to the plates in the short direction. Two-foot centers are fine, since the framing has no structural function. But make sure you can find insulation for 24-inch studding first. If not, use 16-inch centers. Mineral-wool blankets or batts are then stapled to the framing as it is for walls (see next chapter), vapor-barrier side down. The ceiling is then finished with gypsum board or ceiling tile nailed to furring strips.

Another way to insulate a flat roof, particularly if the ceilings are too high anyway, is to hang a suspended ceiling below. Chickenwire is then lashed to the hanging wires, and batts are pushed in above the chickenwire. Some manufacturers make preinsulated ceiling material which can be hung directly on top of an aluminum channel, shown here.

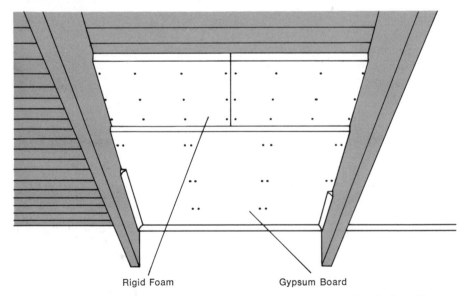

Rigid Foam   Gypsum Board

Rigid plastic foam such as Styrofoam can be nailed or glued directly to cathedral ceilings and covered with ½-inch gypsum board.

Cathedral ceilings. These can be insulated by using rigid plastic foam as described above. If there are natural-wood beams on the ceiling, wood strips or molding can be nailed to sides of beams. Then tongue-and-groove or other wood boards are placed on top of the wood strips. After you get a few feet of boards in place, slide the insulation on top of them.

Before you start this, however, make sure that the beams are made of real wood. Many builders use plastic beams which look like real wood. They won't hold the nails, so you'll have to look for another method.

If your cathedral ceilings are really high, you might even consider eliminating them by installing dropped ceilings as above. Lovely as cathedral ceilings are, they are a tremendous heat-waster. You'll have to choose between aesthetics and economics.

NEW CONSTRUCTION. If you're building an addition, or doing any remodeling work which involves new or refurbished ceilings, this is the best time to make sure of adequate insulation. Since you will probably be closing in the ceilings of any new work, give a hard look to future energy savings. You won't get a second chance.

Consider your insulation requirements at the very first planning session. In the ceiling, for instance, 2×6 joists will probably be adequate for structural purposes. But 2×8s or 2×10s or even 2×12s will let you use much thicker insulation.

Suppose you're adding a family room, for instance. In many cases, you'll want it to be air-conditioned for year-round comfort. If so, R-38 insulation is recommended in the ceiling. To accommodate that much mineral-wool insulation and still have a little ventilation between insulation and roofing, you may need 12-inch rafters or joists. You can, of course, use plastic foam and smaller lumber, but it's wise to do a little comparative shopping first.

Insulation is quick and simple in new work. You will probably find it's easier to staple the insulation to the joists after the roof is on and before the ceiling finish material below is up. If you put up the insulation before the roof is installed, it will be exposed to the elements and may get rain-soaked and worthless.

There are a lot of other energy-saving ideas which can be incorporated into new work. See the next few chapters for wall and floor suggestions, and Chapter 13 for other ideas.

8 | How to Insulate Walls

Of all insulation jobs, finished walls present the most difficulty for the do-it-yourselfer. Access is limited, if not impossible, and in most cases a professional is required. Furthermore, it's not easy to determine how much insulation, if any, is already there.

A simple test on a cold day is simply to touch the wall. If it's ice-cold, there is probably no insulation at all. When in doubt, place one hand on the outside wall and another on an inside partition. If there's a noticeable difference, insulation is either thin or nonexistent.

It's more difficult to tell on a warm day, but you should not wait until subzero weather to decide whether or not you need insulation. One way of checking is to remove a cover plate from a wall switch and peek inside. If you can't tell by looking in, get a flashlight and shine it through one of the holes in the electrical box. (Turn off the juice first, though, to play it safe.)

None of this may work, however, and it may be that you will have to remove some of the woodwork or drill a hole in the gypsum board. You might think you could check from the outside easier by removing a shingle or piece of clapboard, but there'll be sheathing or plywood behind that which you'll also have to go through, so check from the inside.

If you have to disturb the interior finish, do it at the top of the wall. If you do add more insulation yourself, you'll be removing the top portion of the wall anyway.

The odds are great that the insulation is inadequate, and you'll want to add to it in any case. It's probably just as easy to call in an insulating contractor in the beginning and have him check for you. Assuming he's capable and honest (a rather rash assumption), he'll be able to check with a minimum of disturbance to the walls. You'll want to use a reliable contractor, in any case, to blow in some cellulose or foam, so you may as well bite the bullet from the start. If you insist, however, there are ways to do it yourself.

INSULATING FINISHED WALLS. In Chapter 2, balloon-type construction was described. If you have this type of home, you're in luck. Just go into the attic and pour your insulating material down between the studs. Perlite or vermiculite works best here, since these materials are heavy and fluid enough to fill completely and find their way around obstructions.

You may have trouble finding enough of these materials, however, and the price may be way out of range. The next choice is cellulose. As always, make sure that the cellulose is treated with a borax solution to make it fire-resistant. The fire rating should be clearly marked on the bag. Mineral wool in bags may also be used, but it is very lightweight and may not fill as well as you want.

There isn't much to tell you about using any of these materials when you have a clear space between the studs. Simply open the bags and pour until the material fills to the top.

Older homes, where you generally find this type of construction, may also have firestops, cross bracing, or ducts between studs somewhere down below. It will be difficult to determine this even with a flashlight, especially if the obstruction is on the first floor and you're above the second. When you can see that there is an obstruction, you should also attempt to make a hole in the wall below the obstruction and finish the job from there.

In most homes, you will have to remove the top one or two feet of the finish material in order to install the insulating material. For two-story homes, you'll have to do it on both floors. Most walls will be made of gypsum board. To remove this, make a clean cut all across the top of the wall with a utility knife. Several passes may be necessary. Once the cut is made, you can work the top back and forth until it breaks or pulls clear. This is a messy job, so put newspapers on any rugs underneath. Remove all nails and stray material now. It'll have to be done eventually anyway.

It's a lot of work, but you can save some money by removing the upper part of your walls and pouring in your own loose-fill insulation. The diagrams show two ways of removing and replacing wallboard. Mineral-wool batts can be used to insulate the top section. See the text for details.

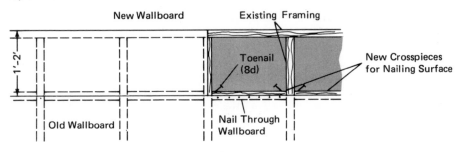

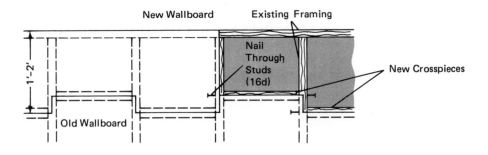

If the walls are paneled, it is best to pull off the panels completely. Take off baseboards and other trim first. Work at a panel corner with a screwdriver or chisel until you have it loose. The rest of the nails will either pop out or pull through. Use your screwdriver, old chisel, or dull wire cutters to pull out the nails.

You could also cut through the paneling at the 2-foot level, but you can't very well patch up the paneling later. It is possible to put up a molding strip over the cut, but it won't look all that great. Sometimes, with high ceilings, the paneling will have been too short anyway, and there'll be molding or a shelf where two pieces of paneling were butted together. In that case, you have a natural place to pull off the paneling and put it back the same way. Even if the space is smaller than the recommended 2 feet, it'll be better to work with the smaller hole than have to patch later.

Paneling may have been put up over the gypsum wallboard. If so, remove two feet of that as outlined above. You don't have to be as careful in removing the wallboard because it won't show later.

Pouring the insulation. Once the cover material is removed, the insulation itself is easy. Just pour it between each stud until it reaches the top. You will probably need a ladder to get the bags high enough.

But what about that last 2 feet which you removed? You can't pour insulation there because you've removed the wallboard which holds it in. The solution is to staple small pieces of batt or blanket insulation in those spaces, getting as high an R as you can. Install the mineral wool as described below for new work.

Patching up the wall. This is the hard part. You now have to fix up the walls so that the patchwork doesn't show. There are a couple of ways to do this, none of them entirely satisfactory.

The professional method is to install new framing at the juncture of the existing wallboard and the new. Using the same lumber as the studs, ordinarily 2×4s, saw a piece to fit between the two studs. The distance should be 14½ inches for relatively new lumber, 14⅝ inches in older homes, but measure each one to make sure. Carpenters aren't perfect either.

Insert the new piece between each stud so that about half of the new cross-member shows above the existing drywall. The new piece is then toenailed to the studs, which isn't easy, since only the top part is accessible. Nailing through the old drywall will help hold the crosspiece while you toenail at the top.

Actually, even though it isn't the best construction practice, you can usually install the new wallboard just by nailing it to the studs. This may result in some buckling and unevenness, but it may be the best compromise. Joint cement should cover up most of your sins.

After you get up the new pieces of gypsum board, the spaces are filled with joint cement. The perforated tape usually associated with this cement can be used but there won't be any beveled edges to serve as an indentation for the tape. There is thin drywall patching tape on the market, which is better for this purpose. Either type will cause a slight bulge. But carefully tapered patch should hide the hump.

In any case, with or without the tape, fill the joint with taping compound or spackle, tapering it away from the edges with a wide drywall knife. Let it dry for a day or so, sand, then put down another layer of the same, more carefully this time because it should be the last. Taper the cement carefully away from the center to minimize any bulges. If you do this skillfully enough, you may not need further sanding. Chances are, though, that you'll have to sand the joint after it dries to get a smooth surface and perhaps need a third coat.

If you work carefully, you should be able to produce a joint that isn't noticeable, but it may be that it still looks unacceptable. There are several ways to mask the joint, if this happens. One is to install a piece of molding all around. A shelf going around the room at that level sometimes looks pretty nice. A "busy" wallpaper should also cover any imperfections. You may even want to run a strip of wall covering just down to the joint. The effect may be pleasantly different or plain awful, depending on your tastes. An imaginative decorator can probably come up with several other ideas.

Repainting. If you're just repainting the wall—and you will certainly have to do that if nothing else—forego the ease of latex paints unless there is a vapor barrier on any pre-existing insulation. Ask your paint dealer for a paint which provides a nonpermeable film that also serves as a vapor barrier. He will probably recommend an oil-base paint. You don't have to do the entire room that way, just the outside walls. You can leave the other walls in a contrasting color, or perhaps find a latex paint that matches the oil-base.

Paneling is replaced the same way it was before. Use nails that match the paneling if possible. Otherwise, use 6d finishing nails, countersink with a nail set, and fill in both the old nailholes and the tops of the new nails with a matching putty stick. If a good match is not available, use wood putty mixed with an oil color or stain. When there is a gypsum backboard behind the paneling, simply nail up a new gypsum board before putting up the paneling. You don't really have to patch up the joints, although a layer of spackle will provide a little more thermal protection.

INSULATING UNFINISHED WALLS. When the studs are exposed, as in an attic room or garage, mineral-wool batts or blankets are the treatment of choice. Compared to the pour method described above, installing the mineral wool is a pleasure.

You'll need a staple gun and utility knife, light gloves, and a loose-fitting long-sleeve shirt and other loose clothing. Eye protection shouldn't be necessary for walls, although a face mask might be in order if you have respiratory problems.

Take one of the blanket rolls or batts and extend it all the way up to the ceiling, making sure to leave no gaps. The vapor barrier, as always, goes on the warm side. Measure the height and cut insulation to size. Put a couple of staples on each side, either at the side of the stud or on the face as shown. Smooth out the rest and continue stapling about every 6 inches. Continue until you get to the bottom, making sure again to get a snug fit, and staple the end. Proceed to the next stud and repeat until the wall is finished. Use scraps to fill in around windows, switches, etc. Either staple through the edge of the vapor barrier, or remove the vapor barrier and cover the unfaced scraps with polyethylene.

MASONRY WALLS. All types of masonry—poured concrete, concrete block, brick, and stone—are poor insulators. The best insulation for brick or stone veneer is pro-

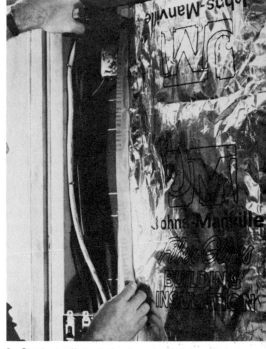

1. Measure the distance between the top and bottom plates and cut the blankets to the correct size.

2. Start stapling at the top, on the face as shown, to achieve a good seal around the vapor barrier.

3. Staple all the way to the bottom, making sure that the entire cavity is filled with insulation.

4. When using the face-stapling method, put the flange of the blanket over the flange of the preceding one.

5 & 6. Odd-sized pieces can be stapled through the vapor barrier (left-hand photo). In very narrow spaces, such as the important areas between the framing and doors and windows, take scraps of unfaced insulation and stuff them into the open places.

fessionally blown-in cellulose or ureaformaldehyde. In some cases, the contractor will work from the inside, blowing his insulation into the interior stud walls. This type of job can also be done from outside by removing brick or drilling through mortar.

Some homes may use stone or interior-faced block as the wall surface, instead of having a stud wall. In that case, you can add rigid foam insulation to the surface as described in Chapter 9 for basement walls. Most brick walls are actually brick veneer, so that insulating materials can be blown between the stud wall and the brick as well as between the studs.

If it's at all possible—and it usually isn't—to gain access to the top of a concrete-block wall, insulating materials can be poured into the cores, or hollow cells, from the top. Perlite or vermiculite is the insulation of choice here. Since it is ordinarily impossible to do this once the wall is up, the usual application is with new work. If planning a new addition using concrete block, it is best to insulate both the cores and the inside face of the block.

NEW WORK. New work is easily insulated, of course, the same way as the exposed studs in the previous section. The time to think about insulation is during the planning stages.

You will note, for example, that the recommended R-value for walls in most parts of the country is 19. This requires 6 inches of mineral wool batts, an impossible task when the walls are nominally 4 inches thick. A 2×4 stud is actually 1½ by 3½ inches, which means that the thickest mineral-wool blanket that can be installed is R-11 or R-13.

If you want your new or renovated room to be cozy and thermally efficient, seriously consider using 6-inch framing for the walls. Here, there's some extra cost. And, for renovation, there's some loss of living space. Adding 2 inches of framing to each outside wall can mean a lot less living area—although not necessarily. It depends on how much room you have. If you are already planning an addition that will go to the limit of the setbacks provided by the building code, that means your living space will have to be cut back 2 inches on that wall. On an 18-foot wall, that's 3 square feet less floor area.

But perhaps you can redesign the room so that the long wall is in the other direction. If there are no limitations with available space, it shouldn't make too much difference. Instead of bringing the room in 2 extra inches, extend the outside walls out an extra 2 inches, leaving the living space the same.

Perhaps even better, although more costly, is to use rigid foam, such as Styrofoam or High-R Sheathing, on the outside of the studs. Follow manufacturer's directions carefully.

You should also consider alternate heating sources for any new work. An addition on the south side of the home, for example, is ideal for solar heating. Instead of adding on to the heating system, perhaps you may want to install a wood stove. If you are interested in such an alternate source, get a book on it.

9 | How to Insulate Floors and Basements

IF YOU WILL STUDY the recommended R-values given in Chapter 4, you will note an interesting difference between northern and southern climates. The suggested R-values for walls almost everywhere is R-19. In the northern areas, floor insulation should exceed wall insulation, whereas in the southern areas, wall insulation should exceed floor insulation.

Obviously, floor insulation is of greater value for preventing heat loss than cooling loss. One reason for this is that the ground itself is a good insulator, staying in all parts of the country and in all seasons at about 55 degrees below the frost level.

When the ground itself freezes, the basement areas get very cold and there is considerable heat loss. In hot weather, the ground stays relatively cool even near the surface. Consequently, there is a considerable flow of heat toward the basement or the ground in cold weather. In warmer weather, the ground stays reasonably cool and there is only minimal air flow from the warmer basement or slab to the air-conditioned upstairs.

The principal objective of floor insulation, therefore, is to prevent warmth from the house from flowing into the ground or basement, and to prevent cold air infiltration into the heated areas.

There are two ways of insulating a home with a basement. The choice depends on whether you use the basement at all for living space, or plan to in the near future.

INSULATING THE FLOOR. The best way of insulating floors and keeping nice warm tootsies in the wintertime is to install mineral-wool batts or blankets between the first-floor joists. This is an easy job, although just a little more complicated than wall insulation.

Vapor barriers, as you will recall, should always be on the warm side. In this case, the warm side is *above* the insulation. You can't attach the insulation in the usual way—stapling to the framing—because that will put the vapor barrier on the cool side. Other methods must be used to hold the insulation in place.

There are several ways of supporting the insulation, and they all work about equally well. All that really matters is that there be something to keep the material from sagging and falling. Actually, the insulation will usually stay there when you put it up because of the friction between the sides of the insulation and the wood. Batts and blankets are just a little bit wider than the space itself.

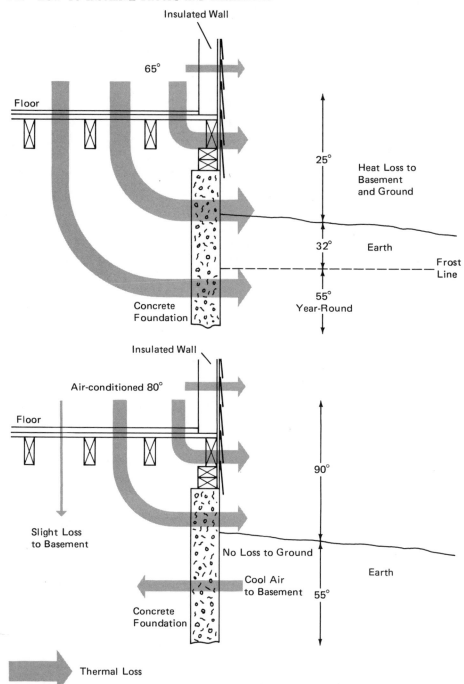

This drawing shows typical thermal losses in winter and summer in an air-conditioned house. Note that the winter heating loss is greater because the ground itself gets cold, while in summer the earth is cooler than the outside air.

When insulating the ground floor, the vapor barrier, as always, goes on the warm side. In this instance, the barrier is at the top, making it impossible to staple through the flanges.

Whether it will stay up there indefinitely is another matter, and some method must be devised of making sure it stays put.

Probably the easiest method is to use "tiger's teeth," bowed wires with pointed ends especially made for this purpose. These are not always available, but other methods are just as good, although a little more time-consuming. One popular device is to staple chickenwire or wire fencing to the bottoms of the joists. The usual method is shown here, but another method is to put up the chickenwire first and slide in the insulation. Another way is to put small common nails every foot or so into the joists and lace thin wire such as picture wire between the nails. You can also use lath, furring strips, or almost anything else that's handy. If you're planning on putting up ceiling tile in the basement, furring strips on 1-foot centers can also serve as stapling strips for the tile. But if you're putting up ceiling tile in the basement, you're doubtless going to use the basement for living space—in which case it is probably a waste to insulate the floors above; you should insulate the basement itself, as described later in this chapter.

You may find some insulation that has a backing material in addition to a vapor barrier. The backing material is permeable and allows air to pass through, but also has flanges for stapling. Simply staple this material up as you would standard batts or blankets.

INSULATING THE BAND JOISTS. Band joists are the 2×8s or 2×10s between the flooring and the wood sill plate that rests on the foundation. The actual wood surface between the outside and the basement area is only 1½ inches, which has an R-factor of only about 1.8. In addition, there is quite a bit of air infiltration through the spaces that inevitably occur where the band joists are nailed top and bottom.

The easiest way to hold up basement insulation is to use the pointed wires known as Tiger's Teeth.

If Tiger's Teeth are not available, perhaps the easiest method is to drive in small common nails and string thin support wire along the nails.

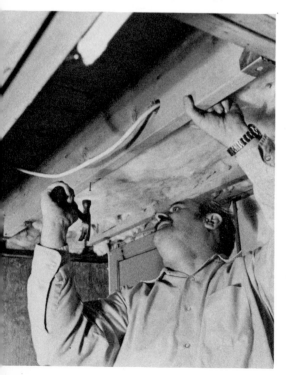

Chickenwire or wire fencing is also used to hold up basement insulation.

The band joists at the ends of the floor joists are easily insulated by simply bringing the floor blankets down to cover the bands and sill plate. The end band joists are insulated by cutting insulation to size and running it along each joist. It doesn't have to be attached to anything. Friction should keep this insulation in place. Remove the vapor barrier or use unfaced insulation to eliminate potential fire hazard from flammable ingredients of the vapor barriers.

Insulating the band joists not only provides additional insurance against heat loss, but also helps prevent air infiltration between any cracks or niches. The band joists *must* be well insulated if you're using the basement for living space or insulating a crawl space.

The thermally leaky band joists should be well stuffed with scraps of unfaced insulation. To get long strips, as at left, slice roll or batt insulation the long way.

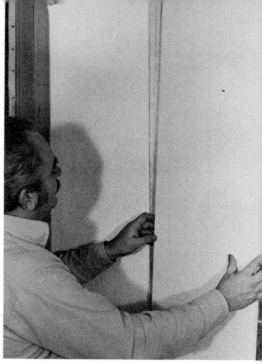

To apply rigid foam on basement walls, spread specially formulated construction adhesive on the concrete in a squiggly pattern, as shown at left. Then press foam insulation into the adhesive.

Furring strips can also be attached to the concrete using the same adhesive. Foam insulation should always be covered by at least ½ inch of gypsum wallboard. In this case, I used vinyl-covered gypsum board.

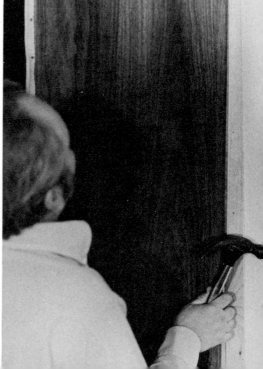

INSULATING BASEMENT LIVING SPACE. When the basement is used for living space, the floor above should not be insulated. In this instance, we insulate the basement walls and the band joists instead.

There are several ways of insulating basements, depending on the finishing methods used. When finishing smooth, level basement walls, furring strips are usually nailed to the concrete and the gypsum board or paneling is nailed to the furring. If nominal 1×2 or 1×3 furring is used, there isn't too much room for insulation. With furring, rigid plastic foam gives the best R-value when installed between the furring strips. The best method here is to use construction adhesive specially formulated for use with foam. Ordinary construction adhesive will destroy the foam. You can use the adhesive for both the furring and the foam. Spread it on the wall with a caulking gun, then alternate the foam and the furring. Plastic foam is available for this express use. It is cut to the exact size for use between furring, and after the first sheet is up, you don't even have to measure.

You don't have to run insulation for basement walls all the way down to the basement floor. All that is necessary is to make sure it extends below the frost line. This usually means about 2 feet below ground level. In colder climates, or on exposed walls, you may want to run it all the way down to be on the safe side. Always cover foam with ½-inch gypsum board.

In some very cold areas, such as Alaska, northern Maine, and Minnesota, it may actually be harmful to insulate the basement walls. The thermal difference between the sides of the concrete can cause cracking of the foundation. Check locally for recommendations on this.

When you use standard 2×3 or 2×4 framing for the basement, mineral-wool batts or blankets are as good as anything. These are stapled to the studs the same as for any wall. Use unfaced scraps to cover the band joists. Short pieces of furring can be used to nail the insulation to the band joists. Since you don't want to compress the insulation too much, use long nails and tap them into the band joists just enough to hold.

If you don't want to construct new framing for your basement walls, but want more insulation than is possible with 1×2 or 1×3 furring, a good compromise is to use larger furring strips. The space then can accommodate R-7 batts or 2-inch rigid foam, which will provide about R-13.

INSULATING A CRAWL SPACE. You *can* insulate a crawl space by putting batts or blankets between the floor joists. Since there is little headroom—and often wet ground beneath—this can be a damp and back-breaking job. Furthermore, this method is more costly than the alternate treatment I recommend.

The best way to insulate a floor over a crawl space is to insulate the walls of the crawl space. The foundation is low and does not require much insulation material. Nobody is going to see the results of this job, so appearance is not important.

Basically, a crawl space is insulated by running blanket insulation down each wall, starting with the band joists, continuing down the inside wall and 2 feet onto the floor of the crawl area. A moisture barrier is used to cover the ground under the floor space unless you have a concrete floor, which is rare. The moisture barrier is usually polyethylene plastic 6 mils thick, although heavy tarpaper will do.

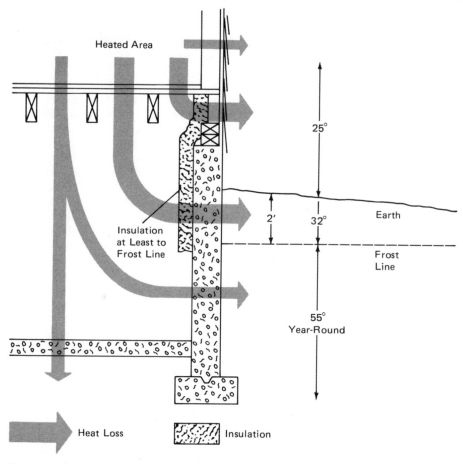

Heated Area

Insulation
at Least to
Frost Line

25°

2'

32°

Earth

Frost
Line

55°
Year-Round

Heat Loss ▮▮▮▮ Insulation

The usual basement wall needs insulation only down to the frost line, in most cases about 2 feet below the ground surface. When the foundation is more exposed, as in raised ranches, the low side of hillside homes, insulation should go all the way down. It's not a bad idea for any basement.

If you use standard 2×3 or 2×4 framing for basement walls, mineral-wool blankets are applied as on any wall.

Crawl spaces can be insulated by putting insulation between the joists, but the limited headroom makes this a difficult job.

Some experts say that you should lay the moisture barrier first, so that you don't disturb the insulation once it's in place. Others feel that it's easier to put the insulation in first, then install the moisture barrier. Although the latter method means lifting up each of the blankets to shove the moisure barrier underneath, I agree that this is preferable to walking all over the plastic film and possibly tearing it up.

If the joists of the crawl space run parallel to the sidewalls, the blankets are started just below the floorboards at the band joists. Tuck them in there temporarily and run the insulation down the walls onto the ground about 2 feet. Cut the roll off there, and continue to the next one. Repeat until the entire wall is covered, then run some furring along the band joist, nailing it with long nails to the wood behind. Don't compress the insulation too much, but drive the nails in just far enough to hold.

Next do the opposite side of the crawl space in the same way, then the third wall, if any. Place the blankets here in the same way as described below for walls where the joists run at right angles to the wall. In the corners, cut off the

It is easier and less expensive to insulate a crawl space along the sidewalls and band joists. Where joists run parallel to the sidewalls, nail the top of the insulation to the band joists with furring, then run down the foundation and 2 feet onto the ground, holding it down with a piece of 2×4, or rocks, or other heavy material.

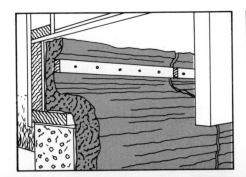

blankets where they meet the ones from the other walls, to avoid duplication.

Where the joists run at right angles to the sidewall, cut off small pieces of insulation to fit snugly against the band joists. Push them into the space between the joists and against the band joists. No nailing is necessary.

Next take one end of the batt or blanket and nail it to the sill plate above the foundation, using pieces of furring and long nails. Don't crush the insulation by nailing too tightly. Let the insulation material roll down the wall and 2 feet onto the ground. Cut it off there, and do the same thing for the rest of the crawl area. There may be small gaps between the strips because of the joists, but you should be able to make adjustments to cover them. If not, fill in between the strips with scraps.

There will probably be one wall where the joists meet at right angles. Here, the insulation is applied as described above. The end strips will be cut short so as not to overlap the ones from the other walls.

Once the insulation is all in place, the polyethylene moisture barrier is laid down. Use the largest sheets available, and overlap at least 6 inches at the seams. Lay boards or rocks over the seams so they don't separate. Lift up the ends of each insulation strip and push the plastic film into the corners, allowing it to lap the sides a few inches to make sure of complete coverage. After the moisture barrier has been put down and smoothed, use rocks, 2×4s, or scrap lumber to hold down the loose ends of the insulating material. It is a good idea—and a requirement of some building codes—to put down a 3-inch layer of ground limestone, sand, or gravel over the moisture barrier. This helps to hold down the plastic and provides something to crawl on when you have to go into the crawl space.

Venting. No matter how dry or well-insulated the crawl space is, some dampness is bound to be present, because the floor is earth. Local building codes determine how many vents there should be and how large. There should be at least two of them to allow cross-ventilation. Most vents are the same size as a concrete block (nominally 8×16 inches) so that they can be easily fitted into a block foundation. If you have no vents, they should be installed. You can do this yourself in a block wall by knocking out one block and installing the vent

When joists run at right angles to the sidewalls, cut off small pieces of insulation and push them into band joist area. Use longer pieces starting at the sole plate and nail to it with furring as shown.

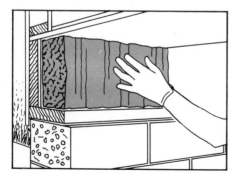 

instead. With a solid concrete wall, get a contractor to do this for you to avoid foundation damage.

By all means, get closeable vents for a crawl space. These can be opened up during warm weather to air out the crawl space and closed up in winter to prevent thermal loss. If the vents you have are not closeable, consider replacing them. Otherwise, it's worthwhile to nail up some plywood or cover them during the winter months. Remove the covering, of course, when the cold months have passed.

One caution here: Check with your furnace man before closing or covering up any crawl-space vents. Some furnaces may draw their combustion air from the crawl space. If so, the vents must be left open all year.

WET BASEMENTS AND CRAWL SPACES. Wet or damp basements and crawl spaces are bad in many ways. The wetness causes great damage to most building materials, particularly insulation. Every effort should be made to cure dampness problems before insulating the floors. You shouldn't even consider finishing the basement or adding insulation to the basement walls or crawl space if there's leakage through the walls.

Damp basements may be caused by leaks, seepage, or condensation. There are as many cures as causes, and it is too complex a topic to discuss in detail here. Below are a few of the most common problems and their cure. If none of these seems to eliminate the problem, see *Expanding the Living Space in Your Home* (Reston, 1976), which I wrote with Richard Demske.

Obvious leaks. When you can see where the water is coming into the basement or crawl space, the best long-term cure is to chisel out the crack with a cold chisel. Undercut the crack in an inverted V to about ½ inch at the surface and 1 inch at the bottom. Clean out the crack completely and flush out dust and chips with a hose. Use a specially formulated patching cement, or make your own out of 1 part cement to 2½ parts sand. Add enough water to make a stiff concrete paste, dampen the crack, and force the mixture into the entire crack with a trowel. Keep damp for a few days to allow the cement to cure.

General, minor seepage. Special concrete paint that is resistant to water, alkali, and mildew can be applied to the wall and should prevent minor dampness. Before using this paint, remove all traces of grease and dirt by scrubbing the concrete with trisodium phosphate (TSP). Apply with a stiff-bristled brush and rinse thoroughly. Wait at least 24 hours before applying the paint to allow the walls to dry.

Condensation. Some condensation is normal in new homes because of the tremendous amount of water used in construction (concrete, plaster, paint, etc.). This should evaporate eventually, but good ventilation will help. If you have a dryer in the basement, make sure it is vented outside. Clothes hung on a line also cause condensation. Opening basement windows or installing an exhaust fan should cure this type of problem. Cold-water pipes often sweat and cause condensation. These should be insulated.

Poor siting. A house set on a low plot of ground will have more problems with dampness than a home on higher ground. If you can slope the ground away from the foundation, do it. Drain tile, properly laid, will help, too. A sump pump may be necessary in extreme cases.

For severe moisture problems, consult a good contractor. A plastic, asphalt, or cement sealer may have to be laid over the outside of your foundation walls. This is a lot of work, and costly, but it may be the only way to solve your problem.

INSULATING A CONCRETE SLAB. If your home is built on a concrete slab without insulation, it is already too late to do the job properly. The correct way to insulate such a home is to put rigid foam between the foundation walls and the slab. This can only be done before the slab is poured, as described later in this chapter.

There is something you can do to alleviate the problem, however, although the result will not be as good as the correct way. Here again we use rigid foam, but installed on the outside of the foundation. To do this, dig down around the foundations until you reach the footings. At least 2-inch-thick foam panels should be used. They are cemented on with the proper adhesive in a caulking gun. It is advisable to cover the exposed foam with some sort of exterior siding material to protect it from damage. No covering is needed below grade.

Many covering materials can be cemented directly to the foam, just as the foam was cemented to the foundation walls. If that is the case, you don't have to worry about nailing surface; just put up the foam boards in whatever way is most convenient. If you're using materials which require a nailing surface, remember to provide nailers at whatever centers are needed for the exterior finish materials. Consult the siding dealer for exact dimensions.

One good material for this is exterior plywood, which can be attached to the foam with adhesive. If the plywood will be in touch with the ground, however, be sure to specify specially treated plywood which is resistant to decay and insects.

Rigid foam, such as Styrofoam, can be glued to the outside of the foundation to insulate a slab home.

NEW WORK. If you are planning an addition to your home which will require a basement, crawl space, or slab, be sure to consider the insulation before you start. No special requirements will be needed for basement or crawl-space insulation, because standard floor joists are always large enough to accommodate whatever insulation is necessary.

For basements and crawl spaces, the thing to consider is the timing of your insulation work. It will be much easier to install insulation in the floor before the subfloor is added, because then you can staple it to the joists from above. Watch the weather reports, though, because the subfloor should be in before it rains. Have some tarps or large plastic sheets handy to throw over the work in case it rains before the insulation is fully protected.

It will also be much easier to put up the insulation in the crawl space before the subfloor is added, because you will have a lot more headroom. But watch the weather, and provide some sort of protection so that the insulation does not get wet before the addition is roofed in. Large plastic sheets are your best bet here.

When putting in a concrete slab, you now have an opportunity to do the job right. Rigid foam should be installed on the inside of the foundation walls before the slab is poured. It is also advisable to put in a base of about 6 inches of gravel under the slab, then lay a heavy polyethylene moisture barrier on top of that. More rigid foam should be placed on top of the moisture barrier before the concrete is poured. Accurate, careful leveling and tamping of the gravel is important so that the foam doesn't break up under the weight of the concrete. *Note:* The polyethylene is used here to keep ground moisture out and is not intended as a vapor barrier, which would always go on the warm side. Foam insulation does not require a vapor barrier.

This is the proper method of insulating a slab for new work. The lined area between foundation and slab is rigid plastic foam. Below the insulation should be 6-mil polyethylene on top of 6 inches of gravel.

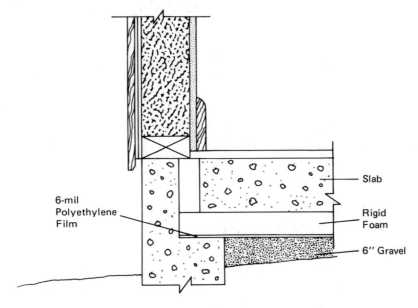

6-mil
Polyethylene
Film

Slab

Rigid
Foam

6″ Gravel

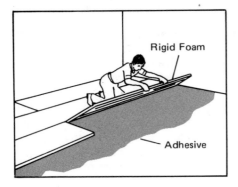
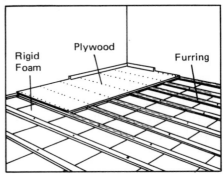

To insulate a concrete floor, lay rigid foam in a bed of compatible adhesive. Furring is glued and nailed to the concrete through the insulation, then plywood is attached to the furring with adhesive and flooring nails.

Because the foam insulation will show at the edges of the slab, extra-thick baseboard and other molding may be necessary around the edges of the upstairs walls to cover the insulation.

CARPETING. In homes where it is difficult to install floor insulation, such as homes on slabs, it helps both comfort and heat retention to carpet as much of the downstairs flooring as possible. Even in the kitchen, carpeting can be used to help ward off chilly feet on cold days. Thick carpeting with a fiber pad is equivalent to about R-2, which isn't a great deal, but it helps. Foam padding reduces the R-value to about 1½, but it's still worthwhile. Even thin carpeting feels warmer to the toes than resilient flooring or hardwood. Slate or brick floors are the coldest of all.

REMODELING GARAGES AND PORCHES. If you are converting your garage or porch into living space, you may well wind up with a cold and thermally leaky concrete floor, which can spoil whatever pleasure is derived from the new living space. The best way to prevent this problem is to insulate this concrete floor. You must plan carefully, however, since this involves raising the floor about 2 inches, which can cause problems with doors, trim, headroom, etc.

It is also possible to insulate basements and even slab floors in the main living area by this same method, but often the problems mentioned above are insurmountable. The only way to figure out the feasibility for your home is to check it out carefully and try to determine for yourself what is involved. You may be able to use the following method in the basement when the ceiling isn't too low, but for slab homes, the problems caused by raising the floor that high will ordinarily be great.

The technique itself is fairly simple. You simply lay rigid plastic foam on the concrete, attaching it with compatible adhesive. Glue and nail furring strips through the insulation with concrete nails on 3-foot centers. Flooring-grade plywood is then glued and nailed to the furring strips with ring or spiral nails every four inches.

Sand the plywood to remove any irregularities, especially at the joints, and lay down some nice warm carpeting. If you prefer resilient flooring, use spackling compound to fill any gaps between the plywood joints before sanding.

114

10 | Weatherstripping

WHILE INSULATION provides protection against thermal loss, it is not any guarantee against air infiltration. Insulation cuts down on heat transfer only by conduction and convection through walls, ceiling, and floor.

Air infiltration, on the other hand, occurs through cracks, holes, and other chinks in the house's armor. On cold days, heated air is allowed to escape through these vulnerable areas. Cold air enters from the outside, causing drafts and forcing the warm air toward the opposite side, where heat is pushed through the chinks in the other side.

There are two ways to stop this type of thermal loss—by weatherstripping and caulking. Weatherstripping is primarily an inside job. Caulking is done outside, and is discussed in the next chapter.

The main task of weatherstripping is to plug up gaps that allow air infiltration at doors and windows—those parts of the house that are movable, and therefore must allow some heat transfer when opened. Doors and windows must open. Otherwise, why have them at all? (This is not necessarily a rhetorical question. See Chapter 14 for a more complete discussion.) But they also should be able to close tightly.

Modern windows are made with spring-metal channels on the side, which both weatherstrip and hold the windows in place.

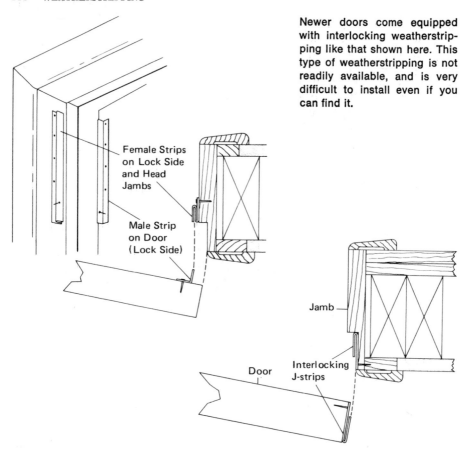

Newer doors come equipped with interlocking weatherstripping like that shown here. This type of weatherstripping is not readily available, and is very difficult to install even if you can find it.

Female Strips on Lock Side and Head Jambs

Male Strip on Door (Lock Side)

Jamb

Door

Interlocking J-strips

TYPES OF WEATHERSTRIPPING. Modern windows and doors usually come with factory-installed weatherstripping that should last for a long time. In some windows the channels in which the sash rides also serve as weatherstripping. Prehung doors may have interlocking channel weatherstripping already in place.

The type of weatherstripping installed at the factory is usually of high quality, but is difficult or impossible for the homeowner to duplicate. Interlocking J-strips, for example, give excellent protection, but the door must be removed and the metal precisely aligned. Even if you are a skilled craftsman, this kind of weatherstripping is very hard to achieve.

The types of weatherstripping available to the homeowner fall into the general categories discussed below. Several manufacturers make these materials, and both price and quality are fairly uniform, so the choice lies not so much in the brand, but in the type.

The things to consider when buying are effectiveness, durability, and ease of installation. If your home needs a lot of weatherstripping, price may also be a factor, but for one or two windows or doors, the price is reasonably low no matter what type you choose. Most materials come in 17-foot rolls, enough for one door or two small windows.

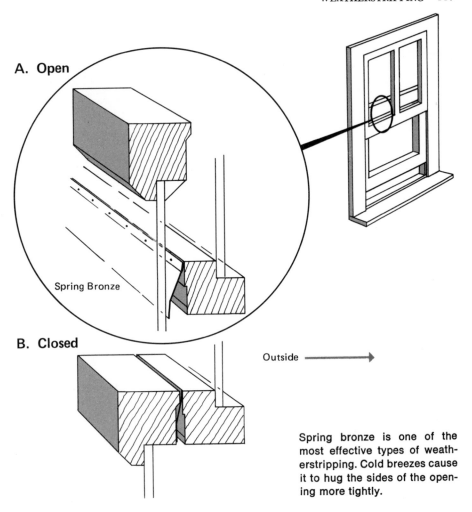

A. Open

Spring Bronze

B. Closed

Outside ⟶

Spring bronze is one of the most effective types of weatherstripping. Cold breezes cause it to hug the sides of the opening more tightly.

Spring bronze. This is probably the most effective and durable of all the do-it-yourself weatherstripping products. It is a little more difficult to apply than the others, but worth the small extra effort.

Spring bronze forms a tight seal between the door or window and the frame, which becomes even tighter when the wind blows because the pressure against the flexible metal holds it tighter against the sides of the opening. This type of weatherstripping is installed in such a way that it cannot be seen when the door or window is closed. It is relatively inexpensive. Spring bronze is not recommended for irregular openings or metal windows.

Sponge tubular gasket. This is basically a piece of sponge vinyl or rubber inside a vinyl tube or gasket, which is formed with a flange. The flange is nailed or stapled to a door or window so that the tube presses lightly against the opening when the door or window is closed.

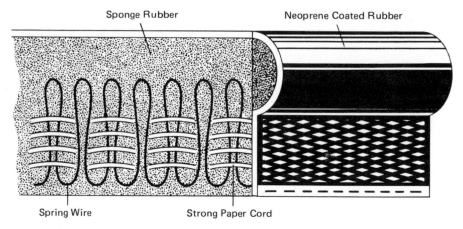

Sponge Rubber   Neoprene Coated Rubber

Spring Wire   Strong Paper Cord

A good sponge-filled tubular gasket has all the features for superior durability.

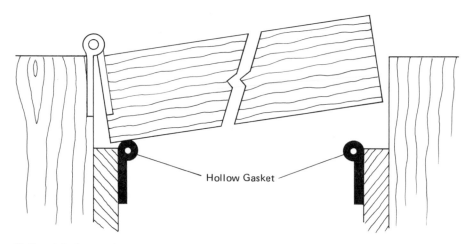

Hollow Gasket

Hollow tubular gasket works in much the same way as the filled gasket, but is not as durable as the filled type.

A filled gasket is second only to spring bronze in effectiveness, and may even be better when the gap is not uniform. The better types have a spring-wire flange, which is very durable. This type of weatherstripping is easy to install and can be used almost anywhere. Unlike spring bronze, it can be glued as well as nailed. It is the most expensive of the types discussed here, and has a rather high visibility.

Hollow tubular gasket. This is similar to the filled gasket above, but without the sponge rubber or vinyl insert. Most hollow gaskets are made without spring wire in the flange, and in general they are not quite as durable as the sponge-filled type. In all other respects, the hollow gasket is a good weatherstripper and has properties similar to the filled gasket. It usually costs less than half as much as the sponge type and may be a good choice where a lot of weatherstripping must be done on short finances.

118

Metal-and-felt weatherstripping is unsightly and tends to wear out quickly, as this strip testifies. It should be replaced, preferably with a more durable and effective type of stripping such as a combination vinyl tube and aluminum.

Felt. One of the oldest and still effective types of weatherstripping, felt is the least expensive of all, and is easy to install. Its chief defect is low durability. Do not use felt where there will be a lot of friction, as at the side of windows. Felt does not weather well, either, so its chief use is at the bottom of windows or on door stops, away from the elements. When used where recommended, felt has a low visibility.

Foam. The easiest of all the weatherstripping materials to install, foam is made of either sponge rubber or foam vinyl. Most types come with adhesive backing, so that the strips are simply pressed into place. Sponge rubber is a little more effective than vinyl, but costs a little more. Neither type is very durable, but people use foam even along the side of windows because the foam is easily pulled off and replaced when it wears out. Because of its low durability, the best uses are the same as for felt. Foam weathers better, however, and can be used outside. If used on the sides of windows, it is highly visible; otherwise visibility is low.

Tape. This is not strictly in the same category as the others. You can't tape over a window opening if you plan to open the window. But weatherstripping tape is quite effective, cheap, and convenient if you want to stop drafts at a difficult window which will probably stay closed all winter. The tape is removed when the weather warms up. Special transparent weatherstripping tape, invisible when applied, is available. You can also use duct or even masking tape on basement windows or other areas where appearance doesn't matter. Obviously, tape can't be used for doors.

Specialized applications. There are several variations of the above materials, such as felt, vinyl, or rubber attached to long wood or metal strips. These are more visible than the materials themselves, but they are simple to apply because only a few nails are needed to put up the strips. One problem is that the weatherstripping material itself may wear out relatively quickly, leaving only a useless piece of wood or aluminum.

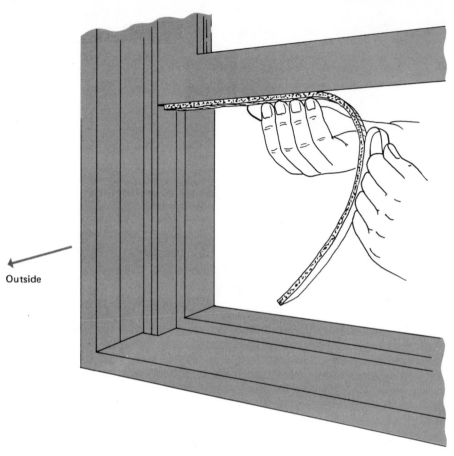

Outside

Foam can be attached either to the bottom of the window or to the sill by peeling off the tape and pressing on the self-contained adhesive.

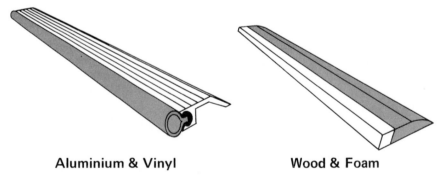

Aluminium & Vinyl   **Wood & Foam**

These long strips are easy to apply. Vinyl-and-aluminum strips are used for metal doors, wood-and-foam strips for wooden doors.

The spring-bronze strips are nailed to the door frame through prepunched holes.

There are also special kits made for uses such as door thresholds, casement and louver windows, and garage-door bottoms and sides, which are discussed later in this chapter. Basically, however, the same materials are used as discussed above.

HOW TO DO IT. Weatherstripping materials vary considerably in price, but even the most expensive types won't break you if you're going to do the job yourself. A major consideration, therefore, is how much work it's going to be.

Installing spring bronze. These metal strips are nailed to the tops, bottoms and sides of each window, and at the top and sides of doors. They are also used at the meeting rails of top and bottom windows. Nail holes are ordinarily prepunched in the metal and the nails are provided with the strip. The nailing edge goes on the inside, so that the strip opens to the outside when sprung. After the strips are all in place, run a screwdriver tip over the outside edge to make the metal spring into position.

Installing tubular gasket. For all types, position the tube so that it is compressed slightly when the door or window is in the closed position. Nail, tack, or staple through the flange about every 4 inches, making sure that the tubular section is slightly compressed in all places as you proceed. Attach to the top and sides of the door frame, not on the door itself. Tack to the bottom of the top window on double-hung windows so that the rounded part covers the crack between meeting rails. The flange can also be glued to the frame of metal casement windows. Use any type of adhesive recommended for use with foam rubber or vinyl.

Installing felt. Felt usually comes with a metal backing strip, which is nailed to a door stop or window bottom. Some felt has no metal backing and can either be nailed through or pressed on with self-adhesive.

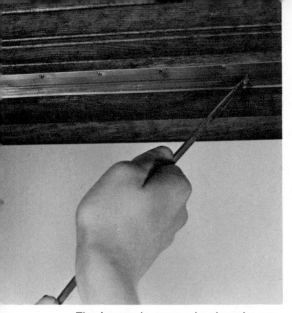

The bronze is sprung in place by running a screwdriver tip over the outside edge of the metal.

Most tubular gasket comes with tacks. This material can also be stapled or glued in place.

Installing foam. Foam ordinarily comes with a self-adhesive backing, which is simply pressed in place. Foam comes in a wide variety of sizes, so try to choose one to fit. It will, however, compress fairly well, and it can be used a little thicker than necessary. One good usage is at window bottoms, where it is pressed onto the sill or window bottom. The window is closed tightly on top of the foam, forming a tight seal. Always clean the area thoroughly before attaching. Otherwise, the adhesive won't stick.

Installing rigid strips. These are usually used on doors, not windows. The aluminum types are used on metal storm doors, the wood type on wooden doors. Kits

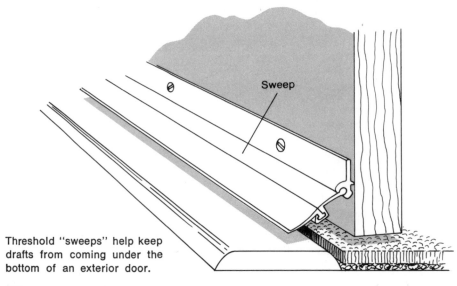

Sweep

Threshold "sweeps" help keep drafts from coming under the bottom of an exterior door.

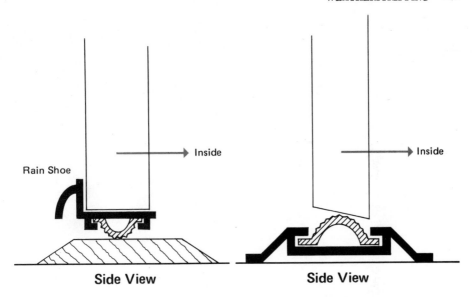

These are the two most common types of vinyl-bulb thresholds. The type that attaches to the door bottom is used when the old threshold is retained. To attach it, you must remove the door. The other type is used when there is no threshold, or when the old one is replaced. The door need not be removed, unless there is not enough clearance. In that case, the door is beveled, as shown.

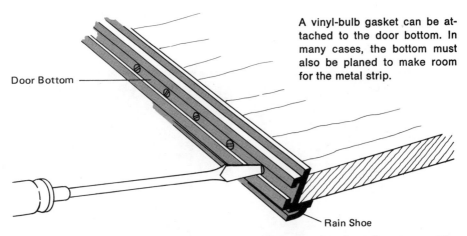

A vinyl-bulb gasket can be attached to the door bottom. In many cases, the bottom must also be planed to make room for the metal strip.

contain one short strip for the top and two larger ones for the sides. Cut to size with a crosscut saw for wood or a hacksaw for metal. Nail to wood or screw to metal so that the weatherstripping material is compressed slightly when the door is closed.

THRESHOLDS. One of the most vulnerable areas to air infiltration is the bottom of doors. Yet this is often the most neglected, mainly because the homeowner doesn't know what to do about it. Ordinary weatherstripping materials won't work there.

This basement door was the source of a lot of cold air from below. The old metal threshold is removed first.

The edges of the door stop on both sides are chiseled out so that the threshold will fit tightly against both sides.

The metal portion of the new threshold is screwed into the flooring.

The vinyl bulb section is inserted into the channel provided.

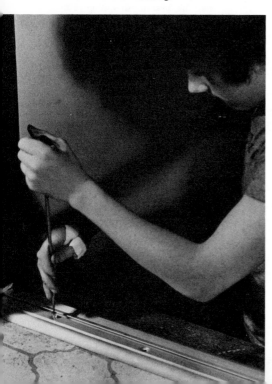

One answer to the dilemma is to use one of the several weatherstripping devices now on the market. Of these, the "sweep" is the most popular and easiest to install. A sweep consists of about an inch of fairly heavy vinyl attached to a piece of aluminum, which is screwed to the inside bottom of the door. Wooden ones are nailed on in the same way. Some come with self-sticking adhesive.

When the door is closed, the sweep helps plug the gap between the door bottom and the floor. One problem is that a strong gust of wind forces the sweep open, defeating its purpose. If the room inside is covered with a rug, the sweep may hang up on the rug. Although it's effective and certainly better than nothing, other types discussed below usually work a little better.

Weatherstripping aluminum thresholds. Installing a weatherstripped threshold can be easy or difficult, depending on the size of the opening and type of threshold already there—if any. Measure the opening and check out both threshold and floor. Is the opening wide enough for the threshold you'd like to install? Must the door be removed? Can the existing threshold be removed easily if necessary? Can you screw through the floor?

One of the best types of threshold is the vinyl bulb. There are several variations of this. Some are installed on the bottom of the door, which necessitates removal of the door and, in some cases, planing off some of the door bottom.

The easiest, and effective as any, of these thresholds is the type which is used as an insert on a new aluminum threshold. Take off the old threshold, if any, and cut the new threshold to size. Screw in the new threshold through the holes

Garage-door weatherstripping consists of flexible vinyl with a rigid vinyl flange. Nail the flange through the prepunched holes.

provided. (Screws are usually provided, also.) Cut the vinyl bulb to size with scissors or knife and push it down into the flanges of the metal. The bulb is flexible enough to seal off any space between the door and the metal. If the threshold is not approximately the right height and length, you can always remove the door and plane it. But, in that case, you may as well buy the type that screws onto the door bottom.

Weatherstripping garage door. There is not much point in weatherstripping a detached garage, unless you want to keep the car warm (which may not be a bad idea when icy blasts blow snow inside). It makes good sense, though, to

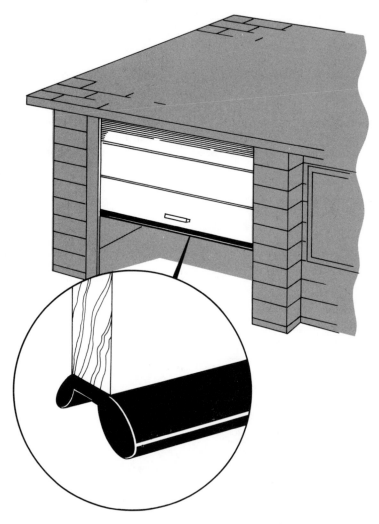

Thick rubber strips at the bottom of garage doors block off drafts and thermal flow even if the space under the door is uneven.

weatherstrip the doors when the garage is attached to the house or located in the basement. The garage then acts as a sort of decompression chamber between the cold outside and the warm house. Weatherstripping the garage doors helps keep cold drafts from the house itself, and retards heat flow from the house to the outside.

There are several types of weatherstripping kits for garage doors. A thick rubber strip is available which is nailed to the bottom of the door. For top and sides, there are flexible vinyl strips attached to rigid vinyl. These come with pre-drilled holes in the rigid vinyl, and are nailed so that the flexible part covers the openings at the top and sides of the garage doors when closed. All can be cut to size with a large shears or metal snips. Long wooden strips similar to those used for regular doors may also be used for garage-door tops and bottoms.

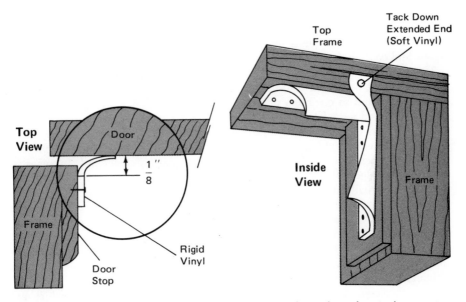

Vinyl strips for sides and top of garage doors are overlapped as shown at corners.

11 | Caulking

CAULKING does for the body of your house what weatherstripping does for the doors and windows. It plugs up cracks and other defects which let heated air escape and cold, drafty, air come in.

There are many places in your home where two different materials come together, where a vertical board meets a horizontal one, where holes were made in the siding, and so on. Each of these meeting points has a strong potential for thermal loss and air infiltration.

The wonders of industrial chemistry have come to our rescue again, this time with caulking compound, a flexible material designed to seal up those cracks and niches. Caulking compound is similar to putty or glazing compound. It comes in tubes or cartridges which fit into a tool called a caulking gun.

Caulk is actually used in several ways around the home. One of the common uses is around the bathtub, where it seems to wear out frequently. This is seen more in newer homes, where stainless-steel tubs have replaced cast-iron ones. Steel tends to give a little when a person gets in the tub, thereby gradually causing the caulk to separate. Here, the usual cure is silicone caulk in a squeeze tube. Oil-based caulk is also sometimes used to fill cracks before interior painting, although spackling compound is more common.

Here, however, we are talking about exterior caulking compounds, which are used primarily for weatherizing. In most instances the caulk will go between two pieces of wood, so that one of the things we look for is paintability. Unfortunately, many of the better caulks, such as silicone, cannot effectively be painted over. Although silicone is a fine and durable caulk, it is not recommended for most applications because of this. There is, however, at least one silicone caulk on the market which claims to be paintable, but silicones in general are considerably higher-priced than the others, and it is doubtful that the extra cost is worth it.

Caulking compounds are usually divided into four groups:

Oil or resin-based. These are lowest in cost and are widely available. They bond to almost all surfaces, but are not as durable as the others.

Latex, butyl, or polyvinyl-based. These are more durable than the first group, but also more expensive.

Elastomeric. These are the most durable and also the most expensive. Some of these are the silicones, polyurethanes, and polysulfides. They can be a little tricky to apply, so study labels.

Filler or rope. These are similar to other caulks but reinforced with fiber, cotton, or sponge rubber. They are packaged in bulk form instead of cartridges. These materials are used for wide cracks or as a backup for the elastomeric types. Oakum is a common fiber type often used to fill larger spaces. Rope caulk comes in rolls and is a good choice where it is difficult to use a caulking gun.

DURABILITY. Although the above comparisons seem valid by most standards and are conventional wisdom, two well-known consumer testing laboratories have done some extensive testing of various caulks, and a review of the findings seems to indicate that there isn't all that great a difference between the less expensive types and the highly touted, allegedly more durable types. Many of these caulks, however, are rated and even guaranteed for a certain number of years—up to 20 years in the case of some of the elastomerics. It is difficult in view of these tests to recommend the high-priced caulks. If you have a particularly troublesome area—along the sides of a chimney is one such place—it is probably worthwhile to try a more expensive type. If you have a lot of caulking to do, the less expensive ones may be a better choice.

Another place where you may wish to try the higher-rated types is on the second floor, or a similar place where you don't want to have to do the job too often. The wisest policy for most average jobs is to use a caulk that is rated somewhere in the middle, such as a vinyl or butyl.

LOADING A CAULKING GUN. Although most of us have seen caulking guns and know what they're used for, it isn't often we get to use one. There are a few things you should know if you aren't exactly an expert marksman with this type of gun.

You probably know, or can figure out, that you have to cut off the end of the cartridge snout. This should be done at an angle, so that the compound comes out in a sort of oval. Don't cut off the plastic too near the end, or the bead will

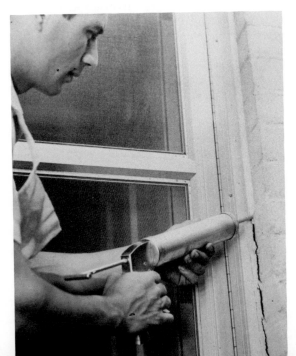

Move the caulking down along the crack smoothly and as rapidly as necessary to lay an even bead.

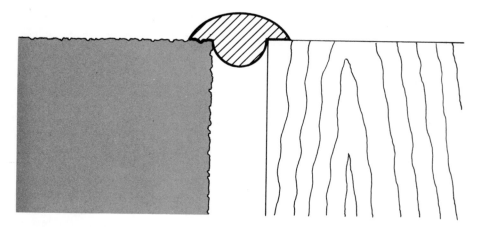

The caulking bead should cover both surfaces on each side of the crack.

be too small. But don't go far down the snout, either, or you'll wind up with a fat discharge that will go all over the place. Although the size of the bead can vary with the width of the crack, a pretty good average is a bead about ¼ inch wide.

The cardboard rear end of the cartridge is movable. The round, flat plate at the end of the gun "bolt" presses this cardboard in and forces the caulk out the other end. The bolt is pushed in by hand until it won't go any further. Then the handle is squeezed, which forces the bolt in by means of a ratchet on the bottom of the bolt. But the bolt won't ratchet until it is in the right position, usually with the bent end of the handle pointed down.

You can probably figure out all of the above by trial and error, but another problem will probably arise which can cause quite a mess unless you understand how the caulking gun works. What often happens is that you've finished laying the bead where you want it to go, and now you want to go on to the next job. But the caulk will keep streaming out the end unless you know how to stop it. Relaxing your grip on the trigger is not enough. You also have to disengage the ratchet by turning the bolt handle to the up position and pulling it back. This will stop the flow of caulk quite quickly.

But what if the caulk doesn't come out at all? That's something else they don't tell you in most of the books. Snipping off the end of the snout isn't enough to get the caulk flowing. In addition, there is a paper membrane inside that you have to puncture. Since it's down where the spout joins the cartridge, you need an extra-long nail or a piece of stiff wire. Once you get down in there far enough, it's easy enough to puncture the end of the tube.

APPLYING THE CAULK. Now that you've mastered the mysteries of the caulking gun, you can proceed with the job itself. If you've never done it before, though, it may help to practice a bit on some scrap lumber or even a piece of newspaper, just to get the hang of it. Caulking isn't at all difficult, really, it's just a little tricky until you get used to it.

Before actually applying the caulk to any cracks, make sure that they are

Many experts say the caulking gun should be pushed away from you as shown.

cleaned out. Use a large screwdriver or putty knife to scrape away dirt, deteriorated old caulk, chipped paint, etc. Hold the gun up to the end of the crack and squeeze the trigger. As the caulk begins to flow, move the gun along the crack as rapidly as need be to lay an even bead. The bead should cover both sides of the crack, but not slobber all over the place.

That's all there is to it, although you may find that you're getting more caulk on the surrounding area than the crack. But just keep trying. Some experts say that the gun should be pushed away from you, but most people find it easier to pull the gun toward them. Try it both ways, and see which works best for you.

If the caulk doesn't get into the crack just right—and it might very well not, even after you've had some practice—you can smooth it out with a wet finger.

Don't, by the way, try to apply caulk when the weather is cold. The temperature should be at least 45°F.

APPLYING ROPE CAULK. Rope-type caulk is perhaps the easiest to apply. Simply unroll it and press it into the crack. Oakum is better for wide cracks. If it doesn't quite fill, put caulking compound over it. Rope caulk is also a good choice for homes with natural cedar shakes. Although some caulks come in colors, most are designed to be painted over. The usual white and other colors

Rope caulk is easily applied by unrolling it and simply pressing it in place.

have a high visibility on unpainted shakes. Rope caulk will still be visible, but the gray color blends in better than ordinary caulk.

WHERE TO CAULK. Almost any house has dozens of places that will benefit from caulking. Check all the following:
- Between window frames and siding or shingles
- Between door frames and siding or shingles
- At corners formed by siding
- At sills where wood meets the foundation
- At water faucet, oil filler pipe, dryer vent, and other breaks in the siding
- Between a porch and the main body of the house
- Where chimney or masonry meets the siding
- Where storm windows meet the window frame (but leave weep holes open at the bottom)
- Where pipes and wires penetrate the ceiling below an unheated attic
- In a heated attic, where the wall meets the eaves and at the gable ends

ESTIMATING CAULKING NEEDS. Because of the varying widths of cracks and the difficulty of getting an even bead, it isn't easy to estimate caulking needs accurately. Most dealers, however, will take back unused cartridges, so it's easier to buy a few extra tubes than to have to run back down for more.

Here are a few rough guidelines:
- one cartridge should do two standard-size windows or doors
- two cartridges for a two-story chimney
- four cartridges for the entire foundation sill

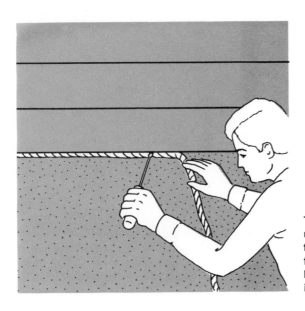

The thicker oakum fill is often used at the top of the foundation to fill the larger cracks found there. Regular caulk can be applied on top of the oakum if needed.

If you prefer the scientific approach, use the following table. It gives the number of linear feet that can be covered by one 11-ounce cartridge. As you can see, the size of the crack makes a huge difference.

LINEAR FEET PER 11 FL. OZ. CAULKING CARTRIDGE

	JOINT WIDTH	1/16"	1/8"	1/4"	1/2"
	1/16"	423	211	105	52
	1/8"	211	105	52	26
JOINT DEPTH	3/16"	141	70	35	17
	1/4"	105	52	26	13
	3/8"	70	35	17	9

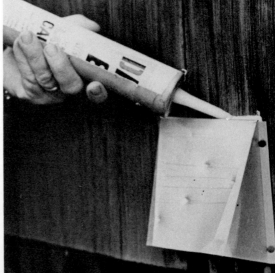

12 | Windows and Doors

IT HAS BEEN MENTIONED several times in the earlier chapters of this book that windows are a prime source of thermal loss. Windows should be one of the primary suspects in any investigation of wasted energy.

There are several reasons for this. First, as discussed previously, glass is a poor insulator. Storm windows are no better, really, but have the advantage of creating an air space between the two windows, which provides a thermal barrier.

But what about storm doors?

We have ignored them so far for a very good reason. They don't help much for weatherization purposes. Many studies have shown that while there is great advantage to installing storm windows, there is very little added thermal protection provided by adding a storm door to most doors.

Note the qualification "most." By that, we mean a normal 2-inch-thick wooden door without windows. Most modern homes have this type of door, which may not be the world's best insulator, but storms don't add that much in R-value.

Some of the newer doors on the market are a distinct improvement over the typical wooden door. Metal doors, by themselves, are probably the worst type of door you can buy, but the newer metal doors are stuffed with urethane or a similar rigid plastic foam. The insulation makes a huge difference.

With either a conventional wooden door or an insulated metal door, a storm door is an expensive luxury. The thermal gain is minimal, particularly when you consider the price of a storm door, which can range from $100 up. Payback on such a door is many decades away.

This doesn't necessarily mean that storm doors are a waste. In the summertime, a cooling breeze through the screen will save a lot on potential air-conditioning costs. (But see below.) That's the screen version, though. Hardly anyone buys a screen door, as such, any more. One buys a combination storm and screen door or nothing at all. The screen door is a reasonable investment. The storm door generally is not.

There are, however, certain types of doors which will benefit from a storm door. One type isn't seen much these days, except on older homes. Glass doors are poor retainers of heat—and a temptation to burglars. Uninsulated metal doors are also candidates for storm-door thermal reinforcement.

A centrally air-conditioned house may also derive some benefit from storm doors. The storms will be effective year-round, preventing not only heat loss, but cooling leaks in the summer. There is usually no point in having screens along with storms in that instance, since the doors should be kept closed at all times. Although there may be a few days when the weather will be just right and you will want to let the breezes in, that type of day is rare in most climates. Check local weather history, however, when you make that decision. A few areas, particularly those close to the sea, may have reasonably good weather much of the year. Since this type of weather is often accompanied by insects, screens may be a good investment. Where bugs are not a nuisance, the doors can simply be left open on good days. The same, incidentally, applies to windows, as well.

Before we proceed to particulars about storm windows and screens, which are the subject of this chapter, we remind you that there are several other steps that can be taken to reduce thermal loss through windows and doors. These are discussed in Chapters 10 and 11.

TYPES OF STORM SASH. When storm sash is mentioned, what comes immediately to mind is combination storms and screens. These are, in fact, the most effective and convenient type of storm sash. They are also the most costly, ranging from at least $30 per window to $100 for doors. The price to equip most homes will range from about $500 to $1000, depending on size and type. If thermal economy is the most important consideration, that kind of money may be better spent elsewhere. You can buy a lot of mineral wool for the same price, and even more weatherstripping and caulk.

If your home is already reasonably well insulated, weatherstripped, and caulked, good storm sash is a solid investment. Well-made and professionally installed storm sash lasts for many years and raises the resale value of the home.

For those with limited funds, however, and a need for other weatherization, the money is better spent elsewhere. What, then, do we do about all those Btus flying out leaky windows? There are a number of things:

• Make sure that the windows are well puttied, with no missing glass.
• Weatherstrip and caulk where needed.
• If feasible, remove the trim and stuff unfaced insulation between the window and the frame. Cover the insulation with polyethylene or weatherstripping tape. This area is a frequent source of heat loss and drafts, since builders usually neglect it.

Once this is done, though, we're still left with a single glass pane with an R-value of less than 1.0. Once the above steps are taken, or even if they aren't, there are other types of storm sash which are considerably cheaper than triple-tracks:

Do-it-yourself aluminum storms. These are available at many hardware and building-supply dealers. You have to be handy with a hacksaw and possess a bit of do-it-yourself skill, but it isn't all that difficult to make storms yourself and save about half the price of contractor-installed storm sash. See below for details.

Rigid interior plastic storms. These are a recent innovation, which can be placed either inside or outside of your regular windows. The better types of plastic—such as acrylic, which does not yellow—are not inexpensive, but the plastic frames which hold them are cheap enough. Even the most expensive materials are a lot less than triple-tracks.

1. To make exterior storms yourself, first cut the aluminum channel to size. Make sure you cut the miter in the right direction.

3. Be gentle when tapping in the corner locks. Held on a bench top as shown, the metal channel takes most of the shock.

2. At the corners of the glass, notch the sides of the vinyl strip neatly so that you can bend it around the corner.

4. Delicate taps along the edges will seat the channel properly all the way around and result in a sound frame.

Polyethylene sheet plastic. This is the quickest and by far the least expensive type of storm sash on the market. It goes up rather easily, although there may be fumbling at first. Sheet plastic gives as much thermal protection as any of the others, too. There are two major drawbacks, however: They are rather unsightly, and they don't last for more than one season, or possibly two seasons.

In addition to the familiar exterior kits with cardboard strips, more permanent types are now available for use on the inside of the house, using aluminum do-it-yourself channel for framing.

The choice between the various types is primarily economic. When money is very tight, opt for the sheet plastic, and bank the savings for other weatherization projects or buy combination triple-tracks in the future. The aluminum and plastic types in various forms are good compromises, but take a little more skill to put together. If no other major weatherization projects need doing, and you can afford them, get contractor-installed triple-tracks.

HOW TO INSTALL THEM. Combination aluminum windows and doors are usually manufactured and installed by a contractor. As usual with any contractor job, check out the contractor's credentials and watch over the job carefully. Make sure that all the corners are well mitered and fitted and that rubber or vinyl weatherstripping surrounds all the glass. See to it that the installer caulks around each outside frame. The windows should have several weep holes at the bottom to release condensation.

Single-pane exterior storms. To make these, first make accurate measurements of the outside of your windows up to the trim. Deduct ¼ inch from each direction. Order enough glass, aluminum framing, and vinyl weatherstripping for each. Have the dealer cut the glass to size. It's much easier than cutting it yourself.

Using a hacksaw and a miter box, cut the aluminum framing to size (using the measurements on the *long* side of the cut). Fit the vinyl over one edge, cut notches at the corner and fit it along the next edge, and so on all the way around the glass. Insert the weatherstripped glass into the longer pieces of aluminum channel. Put the corner locks into the shorter pieces and push into the longer pieces. Tap gently with a soft-faced mallet until they are firmly locked. Install the windows as recommended by the manufacturer.

For permanent installation, lay a bed of caulk both to hold the windows in place and to stop air infiltration. If you wish to make the storm removable, use hangers or other devices as recommended, and be sure to compensate for any difference in the dimensions for the various hanging procedures.

Interior rigid plastic storms. Measure the width of each window to outside of molding. Subtract 1¼ inches to allow for trim. For windows with sills, measure from top of molding to top of sill and subtract ¾ inch. When there are no sills, deduct 1¼ inches as for width. Order a piece of clear plastic that can be cut to this size, and plastic frames to fit on all sides.

Lay the clear plastic sheet on the floor or a large table and mark off dimensions to window size as previously measured. Place a straightedge along the line and run a scribing tool a few times down the edges as directed by the manufacturer. The plastic should snap off cleanly. Some plastic needs a special tool. Others can be scribed with a razor knife, awl, or other sharp instrument. Most acrylic plastic can also be cut with a saber saw and fine-toothed blade.

PLASTIC-CHANNEL INTERIOR STORMS

When making interior rigid plastic storms, first measure width of window to molding and subtract 1¼ inches to allow for trim. Measure height of window from molding to sill and subtract ¾ inch. Where there is no sill, measure to bottom of molding and subtract 1¼ inches.

Measure the rigid plastic sheet on the floor or a table and cut it to size with the special scribing tool available from the storm dealer. Most rigid plastic sheets can also be cut with a fine-tooth blade in a saber saw. Check manufacturer's instructions for proper methods.

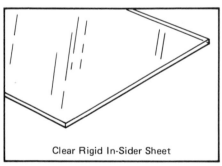

Clear Rigid In-Sider Sheet

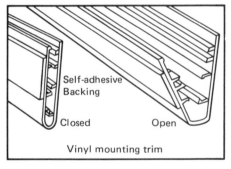

Self-adhesive Backing

Closed   Open

Vinyl mounting trim

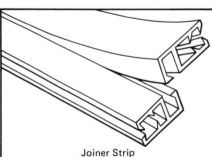

Joiner Strip

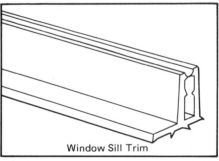

Window Sill Trim

These are the components of Plaskolite's "In-Sider" system.

Plastic trim pieces can usually be cut with scissors.

Now take the plastic trim pieces and cut the side pieces ⅝ inch shorter than the cut window size if there is no sill. If the window has a sill, cut the side pieces 1½ inches shorter. Scissors will cut most pieces, but a hacksaw is best for sill trim.

The top and bottom pieces are also cut ⅝ inch shorter than the width of the clear sheet. Use regular framing material for all sides, unless there is a sill, when a special sill piece is used for the bottom.

All pieces of trim except sill trim are snapped open and assembled on the edges of the large sheet. Use red guidelines for sheet placement. Make sure all trim pieces are centered on each edge. For windows with sills, slide into sill trim first, then assemble as above. Check for proper alignment, then strip the paper off the self-adhesive tape on the backs of the trim pieces and press onto the molding or wall from the bottom up. Press firmly for a tight seal.

Interior sheet plastic with aluminum channel. These make better-looking interior storms than the cheaper outside polyethylene types. They also fit tighter, which means less air leakage and elimination of unsightly sags.

For this type of window, measure the inside dimensions and subtract ¼ inch from each. This allows enough space for the foam weatherstripping tape that goes around the frame.

Using a hacksaw and miter box, cut the aluminum sections to size, remembering that the wider edge of the miter is cut to measured dimensions. Smooth any rough edges with a fine-tooth metal file.

Insert the four corner locks, tapping with a soft-face mallet if necessary. When the frame is complete, cut a section of polyethylene 1 inch bigger on all sides than the edges of the completed frame. Place the frame, groove side up, on a flat surface and lay the polyethylene film over it. Beginning in one corner, lightly press the vinyl spline into the groove.

Using a special spline roller, press down on the vinyl spline and roll into the groove on one side. Then proceed to the opposite side, being careful to keep

Check trim pieces for alignment, then assemble and press "In-Sider" windows into place using the self-adhesive strips on back of each trim piece.

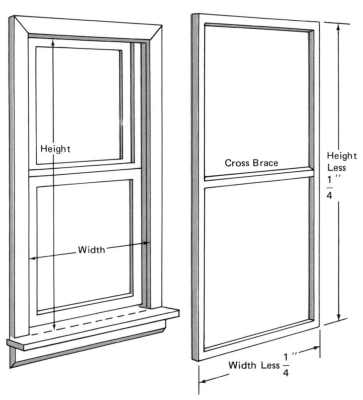

For clear plastic film and aluminum-channel inside windows, measure as shown and deduct ¼ inch from each dimension.

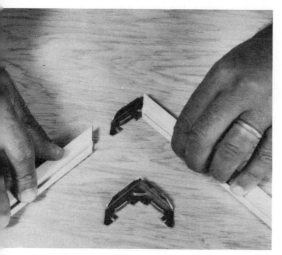 

Cut aluminum channel sections to size; then put together the frame, using corner locks as shown, left. Next, lay clean plastic film over the assembled frame groove side up; then press the vinyl spline into the groove with a special spline roller. Rollers and materials are all available at Reynolds Metal dealers.

Cut off the plastic film at the outside of the spline, shown left. Then attach self-adhesive foam to the outside of the frame.

 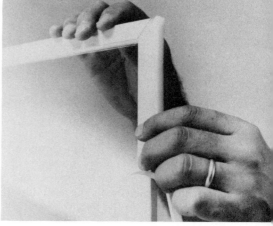

the polyethylene as taut as possible. (But don't pull so hard on the film that you bend the aluminum.) Now do the other sides in the same way.

When the spline is all in place, trim the excess close to the outside edge of the spline. Apply self-adhesive foam to the outside edges of the frame. The window is then simply pressed into the window frame, with the foam acting as a sort of pressure fit. Be careful when pressing not to dislodge the foam. Use a putty knife to help push the foam in if fit is a little too snug.

Incidentally, the solar screen discussed in Chapter 13 is installed using the same procedures. The only difference is that loop hangers are used to install

Press the completed window into place. The foam holds the window in place in addition to providing weatherstripping.

the solar screen instead of foam tape. All parts are available from Reynolds Aluminum and some other dealers.

Exterior sheet plastic. The easiest way of making exterior storm windows out of sheet polyethylene is to buy the kits that are available at most dealers. The "frame" is made of cardboard. The sheet plastic is wrapped around the strips, then stapled or nailed. (Wood furring strips can be used for more permanent installations.)

Measure the window, as always, after determining where you will attach the strips. Cut four pieces of cardboard strip to size, then a piece of the sheeting about 4 inches wider than the actual dimensions in both directions. Wrap the sheeting around one of the cardboard strips and attach to the window. Then do one of the other sides the same way. Next go to the opposite sides, wrap the plastic around one of the strips, and stretch it taut. Nail or staple that side, then do the same with the last side. It is difficult to get the plastic as taut as you'd like, but do the best you can. It'll work just fine even if it's a little loose.

OTHER WINDOW TRICKS. People have been using awnings on their windows for many years, usually without knowing why. Many get them for looks, or just to keep out the sun. Actually, if properly planned, awnings can make a significant contribution to thermal efficiency.

If your home was intelligently built, it should have an overhang on the sunny sides of 3½ to 4½ feet, depending on where you live. About 4 feet is average for most of the United States, with 3½ for the southern states and 4½ for Canada and neighboring states. Without such an overhang, an awning serves a similar purpose.

142

POLYETHYLENE EXTERIOR STORMS

To make a polyethylene exterior storm window, start by wrapping the plastic film around a precut cardboard "frame," shown left. Then staple or tack the cardboard to the outside of the window.

Stretch the polyethylene to one side and staple that, as shown left. Then keeping the plastic film as taut as possible, staple the opposite side and bottom to complete the polyethylene storm.

Winter Sun

Summer Sun

Well-designed eaves take advantage of the fact that the sun is higher in the sky in summer than in winter. Awnings can serve a similar purpose.

Shades and drapes can play a role in reducing thermal loss, while allowing solar heat during sunny hours. And shades need not be ugly. This Breneman "Cabaret" shade is framed by a slim wood lambrequin to give it a custom look. The entire room was created by interior designer Ellen A. Stark.

Shutters can be insulated with rigid plastic foam to reduce heat loss.

The awning or overhang is useful because it takes advantage of the fact that the sun is higher in the sky during the warm months than it is during the winter. When the weather is coldest in the northern hemisphere, the sun is at its lowest trajectory. You can take advantage of solar heat during these months by letting the rays shine through the window. In the summertime, the overhang or awning cuts off the direct rays of the sun, thus keeping radiation through the windows at a minimum. More efficient awnings can be raised and lowered.

Drapes and window shades can also help play a role in allowing or keeping out solar heat. Even in winter, solar radiation can help warm a room, so keep drapes and shades open when the sun is shining into the room, and close them when the sun is in hiding.

A common mistake, by the way, is to have floor-to-ceiling drapes. Since most baseboard radiators are on an outside wall, drapes which hang to the floor will cover the heaters. Keep the drapes at least a couple of inches above the radiators, or tack them up on cold days. It may not look so hot, but it'll keep you hotter.

Does your home have shutters? Most modern homes use them only as decoration, and many are even nailed to the siding so that they don't really work as shutters. If you have them, though, either outside or in, keep them shut in cold weather when the sun is down, and open them when the sunlight is streaming in (and vice-versa on hot days). You can also insulate the shutters with rigid plastic foam to provide extra thermal resistance.

It is recommended safety practice—and the law in some states—to use an acrylic plastic, such as Plexiglas, in storm doors. The little hands shown can push on the plastic without fear of breakage.

REPAIRING OLD OR BROKEN WINDOWS. If your windows are old, leaky, and generally shot, they should really be replaced with modern weatherstripped insulating double glass. If this is too costly, some companies sell replacements for just the sash. Either way, you'll save quite a bit of energy.

Sometimes just the pane itself needs replacing, either because it is broken or because the putty has deteriorated. As mentioned above, there is little point in trying to cut glass yourself. It's a difficult and possibly dangerous operation, which is avoided by having your glass cut to size by a dealer. Just be sure to measure accurately, and deduct $\frac{1}{16}$ inch in each dimension for fitting.

If you've never replaced a window before, you probably never heard of "points" (unless you have a VA or FHA mortgage). The points in this case are little triangular pieces of metal which hold the window in the sash. The reason you wouldn't know about them is that you don't see them. The putty or glazing compound covers them up.

In any case, after the glass is carefully removed (using gloves and newspaper over the glass), the new piece is placed in the molding against a bed of glazing compound. The points are inserted, using a point set, which should come with a box of points. Tap the points in by hitting the point set with a hammer. After the points are inserted every foot or so, apply the glazing compound with a putty knife.

Although it costs quite a bit more, many homeowners prefer to use rigid plastic to replace window glass. In some states, it's mandatory for storm doors. Acrylic plastic is best for storm doors, because it is the most resistant to breakage. Plastic reduces the chance of injury from pushing on a stuck storm door.

13 | Sealing Off Other Sources of Loss

THE MAJOR METHODS of saving energy and fuel costs for the do-it-yourselfer are discussed in the previous chapters. They are, however, not the only ways of sealing off heat loss in your home.

Energy-conscious homeowners will themselves find many energy leaks in their own homes. No two homes are alike, and I can't tell you how to find all of them in yours. Here, though, I will outline a few of the major fuel-guzzlers in most homes, and briefly discuss ways of making them more miserly.

PROPER FIREPLACE AND STOVE USE. Many people think that a working fireplace is a great fuel-saver. And it can be a modest fuel saver if put to intelligent use. Improperly used, though, a fireplace actually wastes more fuel than it saves. The typical brick fireplace, as a matter of fact, is designed more for looks than for economy. Don't misunderstand. I have nothing against good looks. I'm all for them. But my topic is thermal economy, not interior design.

If you have a fireplace or a wood-burning stove or plan to get one, you'd be wise to buy one of the many books on the subject that have recently appeared. There are many variables in fireplace and stove design and use—far too many to cover here. I will, however, mention a few basic considerations:

• Close that damper! All too often, a fire is left burning after everyone goes to bed—the open damper letting warm room air escape all night. Then no one remembers to close the damper in the morning. Lots of hard-earned dollars fly up that chimney. To prevent this forgetfulness, buy a vented-glass fireplace screen or a fire snuffer. The snuffer lets you suffocate the fire and then close the damper before you go to bed.

• A fireplace can provide nice, cozy, inexpensive heat and light on chilly evenings during otherwise warmer months. It can take the place of the furnace on cooler days during late fall and early spring. However, when a fireplace is used along with the heating unit, the heat from the fireplace is minimal. The draft created by the fire sucks in more warm air from other areas of the house and draws it up the chimney, actually wasting more heat than is gained by burning the wood. If you insist on a cozy fire on a cold day—and I love it, too—turn the thermostat way down, and seal off the room with the fireplace as well as you can. Sit close to the fire, because the heat from it is mostly radiant, and directed in a straight line.

• Burn only hardwoods, particularly those with the highest heat equivalents such as ash, oak, and hickory. Split and stack it properly. With the price of fire-wood rising almost as steadily as that of other fuels, it may pay to cut your own, depending on where you live. Many states and communities will allow you to cut down dead or stunted trees on public land. Check locally on this.

• Consider adding devices to make your fireplace more efficient, such as glass screens, thermal grates, blowers, reflecting shields, etc.

• If you don't have a fireplace, but are considering one, opt instead for fire-place stoves such as Franklin types that can be operated in either wasteful fire-place or energy-conserving stove modes.

• Devise a way to direct cold outside air directly into the fire chamber. It also helps to open the clean-out door, which will bring up the colder basement air.

INSULATING PIPES AND DUCTS. As hot-water pipes and warm-air ducts pass through your house, they lose heat. Usually, the loss is relatively small and not worth worrying about. Sometimes, however, the pipes and ducts run through unheated spaces such as crawl spaces or cold basements. Because of the great difference in temperatures here, the thermal flow becomes substantial. The same is true for air-conditioning ducts that pass through attics or other hot areas of the home.

Duct insulation is available for this purpose and should be used. R-8 (2-inch) insulation is recommended for warmer parts of the country, and up to R-32 (8-inch) for very cold regions. In most areas, R-16 (4-inch) is adequate for both warm and cold air. You can save some money by using regular insulation and wrapping it around the ducts. It is less convenient, but it works just as well and costs less.

Cover all seams with duct tape. Use unfaced insulation for warm-air ducts, and a vapor barrier on the outside if the ducts are used for air conditioning.

Hot-water pipes can be insulated with plastic foam that fits right over the pipe and is easy to install. This material is a little expensive, though, compared to the special kits of wrap-on fiberglass with an overwrap of plastic tape. You can even take leftover mineral-wool insulation and use that, covered with duct or electrical tape. It's a little awkward and sloppy-looking, but a great way to utilize what's left of the last roll of insulation.

Cold water pipes should also be tightly insulated, by the way, if you're finish-ing off your basement and covering up the pipes with ceiling material. During hot weather, these pipes will "sweat" and drip down all over your new ceiling.

HOT-WATER HEATERS. For about $20, you can buy an insulation kit that fits right around your hot-water heater. It should save at least $10–$20 a year on fuel bills.

Extreme care must be exercised on gas heaters not to cover up the stack and block the air flow. Electric hot-water heaters pose no special problem, and can even be insulated with standard R-8 unfaced batts. But don't try this on a gas heater.

HEATING UNIT TUNE-UP. There isn't much you can do to keep electric base-board heaters in shape. They either work or they don't. Gas or oil systems that are more than 20 years old should probably be replaced by more efficient, more

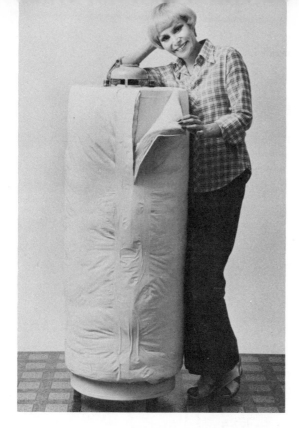

A hot-water heater insulating kit, such as this one from Johns-Manville, costs about $20 and will repay its cost in one to two years.

reliable modern systems. Modern heating units, however, are quite sophisticated devices and require fine tuning to operate at peak efficiency.

There are several things that you can check and fix yourself. Most of us, however, are better off having such work done by a competent expert. Your local gas company may offer this service, often without charge, or may recommend someone. Most oil companies have their own people, and usually charge for this service. Many, however, offer a service contract, by which they will maintain and repair your heating unit for a fixed yearly charge. In case of a serious breakdown, all labor, and in some contracts all parts as well, is free.

A service contract is usually a good investment, because it's in the oil company's best interest to keep your unit in good shape. If it fails, the company has to foot the repair bill.

Those who want to do their own work of this type are advised to consult one of the several books on the topic. A. J. Hand's *Home Energy How-To* (published by Popular Science and Harper & Row) has some good advice for the do-it-yourself heating engineer.

AIR-CONDITIONING UNITS. A malfunctioning air-conditioning unit is another source of thermal loss. I don't recommend fooling around with a central unit, except for replacing the filters as recommended by the manufacturer.

Room air conditioners, however, can be kept in reasonable working order by the homeowner. Mainly, this means changing or cleaning the filters once a month, and cleaning the unit out as needed with a vacuum-cleaner attachment. During the colder months, protect the outside of the air conditioner with a

(*Text continued on page 152*)

COOLING LOAD ESTIMATE FORM

Customer _____ Estimate by _____ Date _____

HEAT GAIN FROM	QUANTITY	FACTORS					Btu/Hr (Quantity x Factor)
		NIGHT	DAY				
			No Shades*	Inside Shades*	Outside Awnings*	(Area x Factor)	
1. WINDOWS: Heat gain from sun.							
Northeast	____ sq ft	0	60	25	20		____
East	____ sq ft	0	80	40	25	____ Use	____
Southeast	____ sq ft	0	75	30	20	____ only	____
South	____ sq ft	0	75	35	20	____ the	____
Southwest	____ sq ft	0	110	45	30	____ largest	____
West	____ sq ft	0	150	65	45	____ load	____
Northwest	____ sq ft	0	120	50	35		____
North	____ sq ft	0	0	0	0		____

*These factors are for single glass only. For glass block, multiply the above factors by 0.5; for double-glass or storm windows, multiply the above factors by 0.8.

HEAT GAIN FROM	QUANTITY	NIGHT	DAY	Btu/Hr
2. WINDOWS: Heat gain by conduction. (Total of all windows.)				
Single glass	____ sq ft	14	. . . . 14	____
Double glass or glass block	____ sq ft	7	. . . . 7	____
3. WALLS: (Based on linear feet of wall.)			Light Construction Heavy Construction	
a. Outside walls				
North exposure	____ ft	30	. . . . . 30 . . . . 20 . . .	____
Other than North exposure	____ ft	30	. . . . . 60 . . . . 30 . . .	____
b. Inside Walls (between conditioned and unconditioned spaces only)	____ ft	30	. . . . 30	____
4. ROOF OR CEILING: (Use one only.)				
a. Roof, uninsulated	____ sq ft	5	. . . . 19	____
b. Roof, 1 inch or more insulation.	____ sq ft	3	. . . . 8	____
c. Ceiling, occupied space above.	____ sq ft	3	. . . . 3	____
d. Ceiling, insulated with attic space above	____ sq ft	4	. . . . 5	____
e. Ceiling, uninsulated, with attic space above	____ sq ft	7	. . . . 12	____
5. FLOOR: (Disregard if floor is directly on ground or over basement.)	____ sq ft	3	. . . . 3	____
6. NUMBER OF PEOPLE:	____	600	. . . . 600	____
7. LIGHTS AND ELECTRICAL EQUIPMENT IN USE	____ watts	3	. . . . 3	____
8. DOORS AND ARCHES CONTINUOUSLY OPEN TO UNCONDITIONED SPACE: (Linear feet of width.)	____ ft	200	. . . . 300	____
9. SUB-TOTAL	x x x x x	x x x x x	x x x x x	____

10. TOTAL COOLING LOAD: (Btu per hour to be used for selection of room air-conditioner(s).) _____ (Item 9) X _____ (Factor from Map) = _____

NOTE: See Reverse side for instructions on use of this form.

Published and distributed by the

Association of Home Appliance Manufacturers
20 North Wacker Drive   Chicago, Illinois 60606

Phone A. C. 312/ 236-2921

INSTRUCTIONS FOR USING COOLING LOAD ESTIMATE FORM
FOR ROOM AIR CONDITIONERS
(FROM AHAM STANDARD RAC-1)

A. This cooling load estimate form is suitable for estimating the cooling load for comfort air-conditioning installations which do not require specific conditions of inside temperature and humidity.

B. The form is based on an outside design temperature of 95 F dry bulb and 75 F wet bulb. It can be used for areas in the continental United States having other outside design temperatures by applying a correction factor for the particular locality as determined from the map.

C. The form includes "day" factors for calculating cooling loads in rooms where daytime comfort is desired (such as living rooms, offices, etc.), as well as "night" factors for calculating cooling loads in rooms where only nighttime comfort is desired (such as bedrooms). "Night" factors should be used only for those applications where comfort air-conditioning is desired during the period from sunset to sunrise.

D. The numbers of the following paragraphs refer to the correspondingly numbered item on the form:

1. Multiply the square feet of window area for each exposure by the applicable factor. The window area is the area of the wall opening in which the window is installed. For windows shaded by inside shades or venetian blinds, use the factor for "Inside Shades." For windows shaded by outside awnings or by both outside awnings and inside shades (or venetian blinds), use the factor for "Outside Awnings." "Single Glass" includes all types of single-thickness windows, and "Double Glass" includes sealed air-space types, storm windows, and glass block. Only one number should be entered in the right-hand column for item 1, and this number should represent *only the exposure with the largest load.*

2. Multiply the total square feet of *all* windows in the room by the applicable factor.

3a. Multiply the total length (linear feet) of all walls exposed to the outside by the applicable factor. Doors should be considered as being part of the wall. Outside walls facing due north should be calculated separately from outside walls facing other directions. Walls which are permanently shaded by adjacent structures should be considered as being "North Exposure." Do not consider trees and shrubbery as providing permanent shading. An uninsulated frame wall or a masonry wall 8 inches or less in thickness is considered "Light Construction." An insulated frame wall or a masonry wall over 8 inches in thickness is considered "Heavy Construction."

3b. Multiply the total length (linear feet) of all inside walls between the space to be conditioned and any unconditioned spaces by the given factor. Do not include inside walls which separate other air-conditioned rooms.

4. Multiply the total square feet of roof or ceiling area by the factor given for the type of construction most nearly describing the particular application. (Use one line only.)

5. Multiply the total square feet of floor area by the factor given. Disregard this item if the floor is directly on the ground or over a basement.

6. Multiply the number of people who normally occupy the space to be air-conditioned by the factor given. Use a minimum of 2 people.

7. Determine the total number of watts for lights and electrical equipment, except the air conditioner itself, that will be *in use* when the room air-conditioning is operating. Multiply the total wattage by the factor given.

8. Multiply the total width (linear feet) of any doors or arches which are continually open to an unconditioned space by the applicable factor.

   NOTE—Where the width of the doors or arches is more than 5 feet, the actual load may exceed the the calculated value. In such cases, both adjoining rooms should be considered as a single large room, and the room air-conditioner unit or units should be selected according to a calculation made on this new basis.

9. Total the loads estimated for the foregoing 8 items.

10. Multiply the sub-total obtained in Item 9 by the proper correction factor, selected from the map, for the particular locality. The result is the total estimated design cooling load in Btu per hour.

E. For best results a room air-conditioner unit or units having a cooling capacity rating (determined in accordance with the **AHAM** Standards Publication for Room Air Conditioners, RAC-1) as close as possible to the estimated load should be selected. In general, a greatly oversized unit which would operate intermittently will be much less satisfactory than one which is slightly undersized and which would operate more nearly continuously.

F. Intermittent loads such as kitchen and laundry equipment are not included in this form.

                                                                     Printed in USA

dustproof and moistureproof cover. Before using it each summer, clean and vacuum it thoroughly. Pay special attention to the outside grille and the outside of the condenser coils so that air flow is not obstructed. Put a few drops of 20-weight oil on the fan motor bearings.

You can get a lot more cooling with less energy if you get an air conditioner with a high energy-efficiency ratio (EER). The EER of all air conditioners should be clearly labeled at the store. The higher-rated units may cost a little more, but they will more than make up the extra price in lower electrical bills.

When buying, also remember to consider all the factors such as size of the area to be cooled, amperage of the circuit, building code restrictions, number of people in the room, summer degree-days, number of openings, etc. All these variables can be charted on the accompanying "Cooling Load Estimate Form." An air conditioner that is too small is almost useless. One that is too big is a waste of money and energy.

In most of the U.S., conditioners that draw 7.5 amperes or less at 115 volts can be connected to household circuits. Some building codes allow up to 12 amperes. No air conditioner rated at more than 12 amperes should be connected to a 15-amp circuit. A 20-amp circuit can handle up to 16 amperes from the air conditioner, but be sure to check local codes on all of this. If you need a bigger unit, have new wiring installed, or switch to two smaller units and use two separate circuits. In any case, don't install any air conditioner on a circuit which already has other high-wattage appliances operating on it. And always use a grounded (three-wire) circuit. All room conditioners come with a three-prong plug that must be connected to a three-hole outlet. Never use "pigtail" grounders for an air conditioner.

It is important to locate an air conditioner properly. If at all possible, use a window that is out of the sun. Avoid the south side of the house unless it's the only window available. Keep the air conditioner in the shade, if any. But also choose a window as close to an appropriate outlet as possible. Try to avoid the use of extension cords. If you must use one, get a cord only as long as necessary—10 feet at the longest—and make sure that it's a new, heavy-duty three-wire extension. Check for the Underwriter's Laboratory (UL) designation.

THE THERMOSTAT. Your home's thermostat is the "brain" of the entire heating system. The thermostat decides when the room is too cold (or too warm, if you have central A/C) and turns on the heating or cooling unit. If it isn't working properly, the entire system can go out of whack.

Thermostats are pretty simple devices, really, but if yours has been installed for a long time, it is possible that it is not doing its job the way it should. It is also possible that it isn't in the right place, which can cause serious problems with the thermal dynamics of the entire house.

Assuming that your heating system was installed by a competent workman, the thermostat is probably in the right place, but it won't hurt to check it out. It should always be on an inside partition, never on an outside wall. It should be 4 to 5 feet above the floor and at least 16 inches away from any outside wall, door, window, or potential drafts. The thermostat should be located as far away as possible from any source of heat such as a radiator, fireplace, television set, or lighting fixture.

Any thermostat that is too near sources of heat or cold will not reflect the overall temperature of the room, which is the criterion it uses to judge whether the heating or cooling unit should be in operation. If the thermostat is fooled by any of these sources, it will call for heat or cooling when it isn't really needed.

The same applies to a thermostat which has a worn or damaged mechanism. If you suspect that your thermostat is getting arteriosclerosis from old age, or that its brain is getting a little addled for any other reason, it is wise to get a new one.

You should set your thermostat back each night. The table here, based on figures supplied by the Energy Research and Development Administration, shows how much fuel you can expect to save, depending on where you live, if you re-

PERCENTAGE OF FUEL SAVED BY LOWERING THERMOSTAT EIGHT HOURS EACH NIGHT

CITY	LOWERED 5°F	LOWERED 10°F
Atlanta	11	15
Boston	7	11
Buffalo	6	10
Chicago	7	11
Cincinnati	8	12
Cleveland	8	12
Columbus	7	11
Dallas	11	15
Denver	7	11
Des Moines	7	11
Detroit	7	11
Kansas City	8	12
Los Angeles	12	16
Louisville	9	13
Madison	5	9
Miami	12	18
Milwaukee	6	10
Minneapolis	5	9
New York	8	12
Omaha	7	11
Philadelphia	8	12
Pittsburgh	7	11
Portland	9	13
Salt Lake City	7	11
San Francisco	10	14
Seattle	8	12
St. Louis	8	12
Syracuse	7	11
Washington, DC	9	13

To avoid rewiring to install a clock-type thermostat, you can buy a timing device which attaches to your present thermostat. This one is battery-operated. Others have a plug which attaches to standard electrical oulet.

duce the setting by 5° or 10° for eight hours out of 24. The savings are greatest in warmer parts of the country, but are still considerable in northern areas.

So whether your thermostat is getting on in years or not, it may pay to replace it with one of the new types which provide for automatic setbacks. These come in several different types.

The simplest, least expensive, and easiest-to-install setback is the semi-automatic type. This has a built-in interval timer, which allows you to turn the temperature down for a certain number of hours. If, for example, you go to bed at 11:00 p.m. and want to get up at 7:00 a.m., you set the dial at seven hours setback. This means that the temperature will go down to the desired nighttime temperature for seven hours. At six o'clock in the morning, the temperature will begin rising to 65°, 68°, or whatever your daytime setting is, giving the house an hour to warm up.

The more popular setback thermostats are the clock types. These turn the thermostat down each night at the same hour, and back up again at the same time each morning. Once you set the times for each setting, it keeps working that way until you decide to change it. Most models provide for only one setback period in 24 hours, but some have two or more, useful for couples that work during the day and want the heat down while they are at the office, but warm when they return.

The main advantage of the clock type is that it doesn't depend on fallible human memory each night. The chief disadvantage is that most types require new wiring. Most thermostats operate on "bell" wiring of only 24 volts, and are easily changeable without electrical hazard, but the clock type requires standard "line" voltage of 115 or 120 volts.

At least one manufacturer, Honeywell, has a thermostat with a battery-operated clock. The built-in quartz battery recharges itself automatically and requires no extra wiring. The Knape & Vogt model illustrated is a battery-operated clock that attaches to your old thermostat and does the same job. Other types plug into a standard outlet.

Perhaps the ultimate in new thermostats is the new solid-state sensor type.

Hot Air Out

Cool Evening Air In

Vents and fans assist the natural air flow on hot summer nights and cool off hot rooms faster.

Instead of the usual bimetallic coil, it uses preset thermometerlike sensors, which activate the heating circuit when the temperature reaches a certain level. These are available with from one to four sensors for the home from PSG Industries, 1225 Tunnel Rd., Perkasie, PA 18944.

FANS AND VENTILATORS. In our modern era of artificial heat and cooling, the old-fashioned fan has often been forgotten. This is too bad, because fans can be used to good effect in hot weather at substantially less cost than air conditioners. A fan is particularly useful at night to draw in cool air and expel hot air. Upstairs fans should exhaust out, downstairs fans blow in, creating a continuous flow of cold air from the lower rooms, displacing the hotter air upstairs. A similar effect can be gained in one-story homes by placing the fans in different parts of the house—with the doors and windows open, of course. The same principles can apply within a single room.

Of all the types of fans, probably the most useful is the attic fan. Hot air beating on the roof all day results in an extremely high temperature within the attic area. Insulation will help keep the hot air away from the rooms below, but an attic fan can help keep the pressure off by ejecting the hot air. When the outside temperature is 95 degrees, the attic can be 150 degrees. These fans are mounted high on the attic wall or through the roof and are controlled manually or by a thermostatically activated switch. Some such fans are powerful enough to cool the entire house.

Since the air that the fan exhausts must come from somewhere, plenty of louver area must be provided in the attic space. If a fan exhausts 1400 cubic feet per minute, for example, it needs 4 square feet of inlet area. Any ventilating system will also increase the risk of fire spreading. It is wise to install an automatic disconnect switch that will shut off the fan in case of fire.

An excellent cooling device not often seen in homes is the "top hat" ventilator. You've probably seen them on farm or industrial buildings. They are actually wind-activated turbines that require no electricity. The wind rotates the blades,

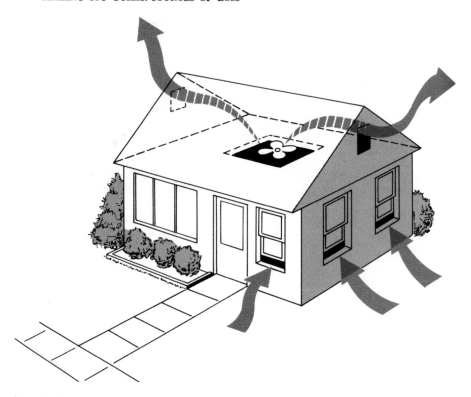

An attic fan can be used to cool off an entire house. When such a fan is intended to cool the attic only, it is mounted on the roof, and cool air is drawn through the vents.

drawing warm air up and out of the attic. Thermostatically controlled roof dampers are another type of attic-cooling device. They may look strange on a home, but energy shortages and high electrical costs may make them more acceptable for residential use.

LANDSCAPING. At first blush, it would seem that landscaping has little to do with energy consciousness. In fact, landscaping can make a big difference in energy costs and home comfort.

Not that you should rush out and buy a dozen shade trees. You couldn't get your money back from such an investment in a lifetime. But most people landscape anyway. Why not do it in such a way that the landscaping keeps you cooler in summer and warmer in the winter at the same time?

It's really quite simple. The main idea is to plant trees and shrubs so that they shade the house in the hot weather and ward off chilling breezes in the winter. Deciduous, or leaf-shedding, trees provide summer shade and allow solar heating in winter when the limbs are bare. They should be planted on the southern part of the lot so that they will arch over the roof someday. Evergreens are best on the north and west, where they will help block off the winter storms.

Wind-actuated turbine-type ventilators are more common on farms and industrial buildings than on houses, but they are practical for houses too.

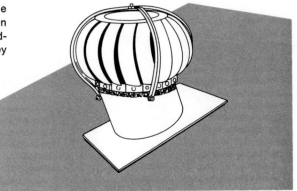

This ventilator, a "Thinking Cap" by American Energy Products, has a thermostatically controlled damper which opens and closes as needed.

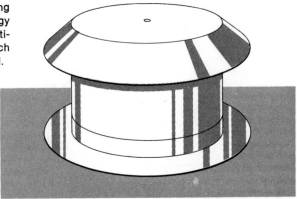

Evergreens 2 to 4 feet tall are quite reasonably priced, and will form an effective windbreak in a few years. A dense row of evergreen trees planted 50 feet from the house will check the wind for about eight times its height. In other words, a 10-foot-high windbreak will be effective for about 80 feet on the lee side (toward the house). The best trees for a windbreak are hemlock, fir, and spruce. Pine is not as effective because it tends to grow higher branches as it matures, leaving the lower trunk bare.

A dense foundation planting of yews or similar evergreen creates dead-air space between the shrubs and the house, thus providing additional "insulation" as well as wind protection.

According to the Cornell University Cooperative Extension Service, deciduous shade trees are seven times more effective than shades or draperies in blocking out the rays of the summer sun. Mature trees can also help prevent heat buildup in attics, if planted correctly. The best trees for this purpose in the colder regions are maples (except the weak silver maple), oaks, and little-leaf linden.

Dense foundation plantings provide insulating qualities by creating dead-air space (small arrow), and also serve as a windbreak (large arrow).

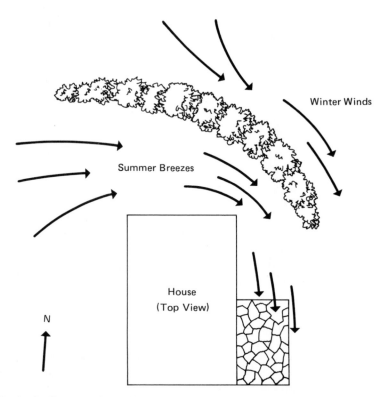

Intelligent plantings, such as the hedge shown, not only ward off the winter winds from the north, but also divert cooling summer breezes to desired areas of the home such as the patio.

An entry airlock helps prevent air infiltration through the front door. Such a room can be used as a mudroom and storeroom, and also as a greenhouse in summer.

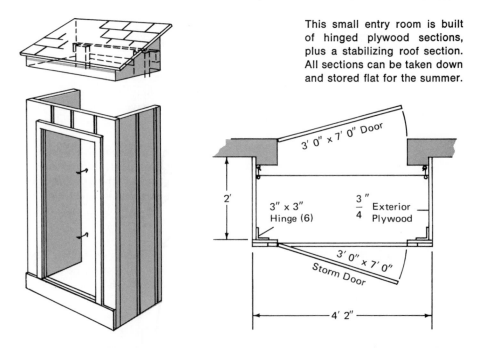

This small entry room is built of hinged plywood sections, plus a stabilizing roof section. All sections can be taken down and stored flat for the summer.

Curved, high hedges can also be planted in such a way as to catch the cooling summer breezes and ward off the bitter winter winds. The hedge shown in the drawing curves from the northwest to the southeast. As shown by the arrows, more westerly summer breezes are deflected toward the house and patio, while the harsher, northerly winds are shunted away from the living quarters.

ENTRY AIRLOCKS. When you open your front door, do you get a blast of icy air into the living room? Most older homes had vestibules and foyers to guard

Special solar screens not only keep out bugs, but divert as much as 75 percent of the sun's rays.

against this. These rooms not only provided an airlock "pressure chamber," but were fine places to store wet boots, snowy overcoats, and dripping umbrellas. Such a room can be used to store firewood or as a greenhouse. You can create a vestibule of your own by enclosing the front stoop or small porch that usually fronts a modern home. Simply frame in the stoop or porch, and build a roof if there isn't one there already. Add a storm door and you have a convenient entry room, which also serves as an airlock to keep away winter's worst. Or add a new closed-in porch if your home doesn't already have one.

You don't like the looks of a tacked-on entryway? Try a portable one. The portable version shown is made of three plywood walls that are hinged to fold and store flat. It's attached to the house by six screw-eyes on the existing framing. The roof section slips over the top of the plywood sections and also gives the frame rigidity. Use duct tape as weatherstripping. Pull it off in spring, and take the whole assembly down for storage.

SOLAR SCREENING. This is a new product from the Reynolds Metals Company. It is reported to block out as much as 75 percent of the sun's heat before it reaches a window. It is installed in standard aluminum channel, the same framing that is used to make your own storm windows (see Chapter 12). The solar screen, in addition to deflecting the sun's rays, also does the old job of regular screening—keeping out the bugs.

I have mentioned just a few of the major ways of saving energy in the home. There are hundreds more. Some save just a little bit, others save a lot. Most are worth the small cost. Some cost nothing, such as an earth berth or intelligent use of appliances. Many have multiple purposes, such as a basement-window well cover. This clear, hard plastic dome keeps out debris from a window well, and also acts as a storm window. There are surely many more gadgets in the works, as well as new technology in both thermal savings and sources of energy. That's the topic of the next chapter.

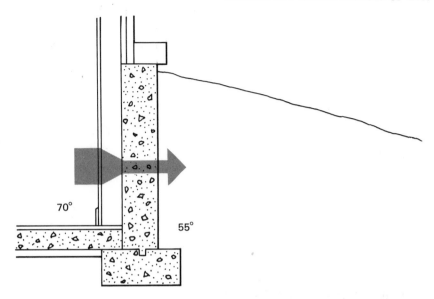

70°

55°

Heat losses through foundation walls can be cut up to 15 percent by the use of earth berms. This simple, inexpensive measure lowers the differential between outside and inside air to 15° in the example shown. On cold days, there is an enormous reduction of thermal loss. Also, on hot days, the outside temperature of the walls is always a cool 55°.

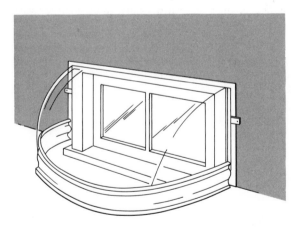

Another inexpensive device is this window-well cover from the APC Corporation. It acts as a storm window while keeping dirt and debris out of the window well.

14 | Looking into the Future

THE PRIMARY PURPOSE of this book is to assist the homeowner to detect thermal losses and correct them. At the same time, however, we all worry about what will happen in the future. If we move into a new house, for example, will we have to do the same things all over again? Is there any hope for new energy forms? What is technology doing about more efficient ways of heating and cooling homes in the days ahead?

Obviously, none of these questions can be fully answered in one chapter—even if anyone knew all the answers. What I can and will do here is take a quick peek into the crystal ball and see if there is any hope. If so, in what form?

HOMES OF THE FUTURE. Homebuilders, based on rueful experiences of the past, are notoriously conservative in the types of homes they build. One of the anomalies of the human personality is that, no matter how radical or creative

Although it looks like just any ordinary house, this experimental energy-efficient residence was erected by Brookhaven National Laboratory in cooperation with the Long Island Builders Institute and many other organizations to demonstrate the effectiveness of energy-saving construction.

New energy-conscious house builders are expected to make use of materials such as exterior rigid plastic foam sheathing.

people are generally, they almost invariably choose a type of home that is not too much different from their neighbor's.

In spite of this, some new energy-efficient homes have appeared in various places throughout the country. Just as many homebuyers insist on a basement or dining room that they may never use, they may well resist the many energy-saving innovations that are being optimistically designed by some planners.

But the new structural changes make a lot of sense economically. It may be that future homebuyers will be convinced of the wisdom of 2×6 studding if it will save them money. But slab homes and homes without dining rooms also make sense economically, and they are far from universally accepted.

In any case, many interested organizations have done considerable research into homes that are more thermally efficient. Time alone will tell about their acceptance generally.

A major feature of most of the experimental models is 2×6 wall framing on 24-inch centers. As discussed previously, walls of that size will permit R-19 insulation, which is recommended in most parts of the country. Another major feature of the experimental homes is reduced window area. Instead of the usual 16–20 percent of the floor area, the famous "Arkansas home," for example, has only 8 percent, concentrated on the south wall. Most energy-efficient homes favor use of the new, improved heat pumps, which also operate as central air-conditioning units at a lower cost. The ceiling insulating recommendations for new experimental homes is R-38. Many envision use of rigid foam insulation outside the studs in conjunction with mineral wool inside.

A typical energy-efficient wall was designed by the National Association of Home Builders (NAHB) under a contract from the Department of Housing and Urban Development (HUD). It has many unusual features, including use of adhesive seals at the sill and bottom plates. Perhaps the most radical departure is the use of plywood box headers, insulated inside, above the windows and doors. (In standard construction, headers are solid wood, even where this means much heavier lumber than the span requires for strength, because one-piece headers take less time to put up.) The concrete-block foundation walls are parged with a stucco finish on the outside to cut down on infiltration. Even the height

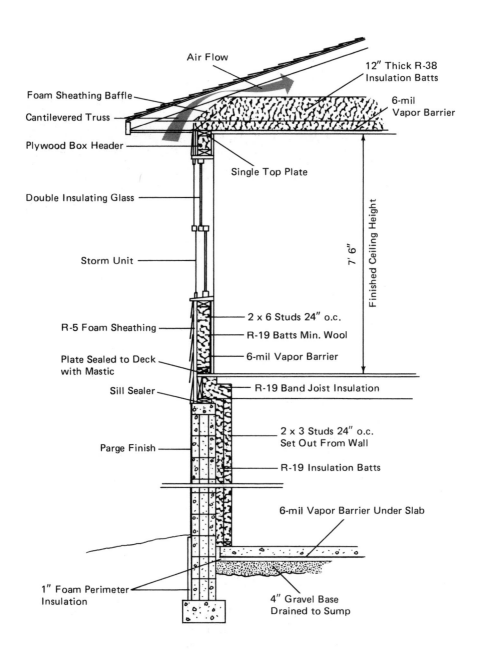

The National Association of Home Builders, under a contract with HUD, designed this energy-efficient residence wall.

of the rooms is cut down 6 inches from the usual 8 feet to reduce interior volume.

Among other recommendations for new energy-saving homes are:

- Roof trusses cantilevered to allow for insulation over the exterior wall
- Insulated metal doors
- Attic trap doors outside of heated area
- Drywall clips at wall intersections to avoid extra nailing-surface framing and allow more insulation.

There are numerous other recommendations, and those who are interested in building or buying this type of home should contact their local energy office, utility, builder's association, or one of the agencies involved.

SOLAR HEATING. At this time, solar heat is still relatively expensive compared to conventional methods. Technology seems to be rapidly closing this gap, however, at least to the point where solar heat is practical for hot-water heating or as a backup for conventional heating. Solar heat is now being used economically for heating swimming pools, too. In fact, pools themselves can be used as solar collectors.

Solar heat does have one serious drawback for long-range universal use. In order to take advantage of solar heat, you need sun, and lots of it. The sun seems more available exactly in those areas that need it the least, like the deserts of the Far West. Buffalo, for example, which could really take advantage of free heat in the winter, has the fewest hours of sunshine of any city in the U.S. Crowded urban areas with tall buildings have a similar problem.

If you're thinking of experimenting with a solar-heating unit, by all means choose a site that gets plenty of sunshine, especially on the south side. Those lovely trees which provide so much shade and a cool attic will also make solar heat a poor bet. And read up thoroughly on the subject.

NEW ENERGY SOURCES. Much has been said already in this volume about the future of energy prices. There is no getting away from the gloomy assessment that scarcities will continue, with attendant high prices. Even with discoveries of new oil fields or a boom in such sources as nuclear power, there is little hope of any leveling off in prices in the foreseeable future.

The Carter energy plan places great hope in our vast reserves of coal. But there are a lot of problems there, as the coal strike in early 1978 brought to our attention. Coal is dirty, and strip-mining techniques are environmentally hazardous. Deep mining is expensive in terms of dollars, labor, and human lives. And one of the biggest problems is the poor condition of our railroads, which will be needed to bring the coal to areas where it is most needed.

Ironically, one of the world's greatest sources of oil lies untouched in the mountains of Colorado, Wyoming, and Utah. It is shale oil, an odd geological combination of shale rock and kerogen, an organic compound that yields petroleum when chemically broken down. More oil is locked in this kerogenous rock than exists in all of the other oil fields of the world combined, enough to last another century, but the cost of extracting it has just been too great so far. Every few years, another company announces that it has a way of economically utilizing shale oil, but it never seems to work out that way. If a way is ever found—and lots of companies are working on it—the pressure on energy prices may ease considerably. But it will be a long, long time before oil shale can make a significant contribution to our needs—as is the case with oil sands.

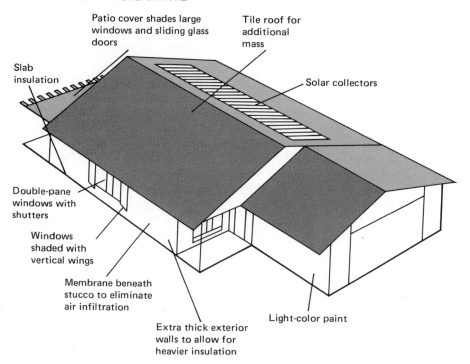

Patio cover shades large windows and sliding glass doors

Tile roof for additional mass

Slab insulation

Solar collectors

Double-pane windows with shutters

Windows shaded with vertical wings

Membrane beneath stucco to eliminate air infiltration

Extra thick exterior walls to allow for heavier insulation

Light-color paint

Lest we think that only the colder parts of the country are being scrutinized for energy savings, here is a diagram of the Minimum Energy Dwelling (MED) designed for the California area by the Southern California Gas Company, ERDA, and the Mission Viejo Company.

Many different companies are looking all the time for new oil fields, or attempting to gain access to known deposits offshore, but even if all the drilling rigs were successful—impossible with the best of luck—we would continue to be in dire need of oil. Old wells are running out faster than new ones can replace them.

There has been a lot of research and speculation about more exotic energy sources, such as giant windmills, tidal dams, immense solar-heat satellites, and others. Geothermal plants are already in operation in some Western states, but the long-range benefit is expected to be slight. Indeed, there is little hope at the present time that any of the more exotic sources will provide anything but a minimum of local requirements. For a long time to come, we will have to be dependent on conventional sources such as oil, natural gas, and coal. Nuclear energy, in spite of high hopes, has been disappointing in terms of costs, and there are grave doubts about the safety of such plants. We will, however, be using more of this type of power in the future, and "nukes," along with coal, seem to be the only reasonable source for the next century.

So we go back to square one. While there is enough long-range hope so that we can reject the doomsday predictions of a world without energy, there is certainly little basis for complacency. As far ahead as we can see, the energy picture is far from bright. There is only one way to make the future tolerable. That is to do everything we can toward conserving the energy we have. I hope this book will be of some help in achieving that goal.

Index

Agriculture, Department of, 21
Air-conditioning units, 149–152
Air film and spaces, R-values of, 40
Air infiltration:
  cost of reducing, 51
  heat losses and potential savings, 29, 37, 44
  through thresholds, 123–126
Aluminum storms, 51, 135, 137
Aluminum thresholds, 125–126
Aluminum weatherstripping, 119, 122
Arab oil embargo, 2
Association of Home Appliance Manufacturers, 152
Attached garages, 17–18
Attic fans, 155
Attic insulation, 65–89
  annual dollar savings from, 8–10
  building attic rooms, 83–86
  end walls, 86
  finished attics, 13, 86–88
  floored attics, 13, 80–83
  inspection of, 10–13
  payback period, 48
  rafters, 86, 88
  trap doors, 88–89
  unfloored attics, 65–80
Awnings, 142–145

"Balloon" construction, 13
Balloon-type construction, 13, 94
Band joists, 103–105
Basement insulation:
  inspection of, 13–14
  living space, 107
  wetness and, 111
Batt insulation, 55
  R-values of, 12, 40, See also Mineral wool
Blanket insulation, 55
  R-values of, 12, 40, See also Mineral wool
Blown-in insulation:
  cellulose, 59–62, 82, 97
  cost estimation, 51
  floored attics, 81

mineral wool, 55, 57, 62–63
perlite, 55, 59
R-values of, 40
vermiculite, 55, 59
Borax, 55, 58
Building materials, R-values of, 40
Butyl-based caulk, 128

Carpeting, 114
Carter, Jimmy, 2, 165
Cathedral ceilings, 93
Caulking, 15–16, 24, 128–133
  caulk application, 130–131
  compounds, 128–129
  durability, 129
  estimating needs, 132–133
  loading caulking guns, 129–130
  rope caulk application, 131–132
  where to caulk, 132
Ceiling insulation, 65–93
  from above, see Attic insulation
  from below, 89–93
  conduction losses and potential savings, 35–37, 41
  cost of, 51
  new construction, 93
Cellulose, 57–58
  attic insulation, 80, 82
  blown-in, 59–62, 82, 97
  compared to other insulating materials, 55
  cost of, 64
  poured, 55, 57–58, 80, 94–96
  R-values for, 112
Certain-Teed, 55
CETA (Comprehensive Employment Training Administration), 20
Changing Times, 5
Clapboard, inspection of, 15–16
Collateral loan, 23
Concrete, as insulator, 14
Concrete slab insulation, 15
Condensation, 111
Conduction:
  computation of, 26, 41–46
  defined, 25